OUT ON A LIMB

and other stories

Enjoy!
Robert Loesch

ALSO BY ROBERT LOESCH

One Year: The Ministries of One Parish and Pastor

***

The Day the Drum Stopped and Other Stories

OUT — ON A — LIMB

and other stories

ROBERT LOESCH

Out on a Limb and Other Stories is a work of fiction.
Names, characters, places and incidents are the products of the author's imagination or are used fictitiously. Any resemblance to actual events, locales, or persons, living or dead, is entirely coincidental.

Book design by The Troy Book Makers

Printed in the United States of America

The Troy Book Makers • Troy, New York • thetroybookmakers.com

To order additional copies of this title, contact your favorite local bookstore or visit www.shoptbmbooks.com or contact the author at: Robert Loesch, 385 Worthington St, Unit 3E, Springfield, MA 01103; rkloesch@aol.com, (518) 674-8204

ISBN: 978-1-61468-527-2

DEDICATED

TO THE MEMORY OF WILLIAM RUSSELL LOESCH (1941-2018)

My beloved twin brother, life-long friend and soulmate
who selflessly served others his whole life

He embodied the values of "love, joy, peace, patience,
kindness, generosity, faithfulness, gentleness and self-control"
(Letter of Paul to the Galatians 5:22)

CONTENTS

PREFACE

Originally, I subtitled this collection of nine short stories cryptically: 2nd D, 21st C. The stories take place in the second decade of the 21st century from 2010-2019. They all take place in western Massachusetts, specifically in the communities of Agawam, Springfield, Westfield, West Springfield and Wilbraham.

Although most of the settings are real places, all of the characters are fictional. These stories share the individual personal experiences of ordinary people living in our contemporary period representing a diversity of faith communities, racial or ethnic backgrounds, socio-economic levels, ages, occupations and education. Seven of these stories are told in the first person by one of the main characters.

I wrote this collection of stories to entertain and inform my readers. Each of these stories depicts characters who deal with important daily and contemporary situations and problems that are representative of many people. I have enjoyed creating and writing these stories. I hope that they entertain and help you, the reader, navigate through your own daily life in positive ways.

I was born in Florida and graduated from schools in Massachusetts, New Jersey, Ohio and Connecticut. I have worked lived and worked in New England and upstate New York. Most of my career has been in parish ministry and human services. I have traveled in forty-nine states of the United States and in over forty nations. I have lived in Springfield, Massachusetts for more than twenty-six years. Most of my published writing since 1966 has been in non-fiction. This is my second collection of short stories.

OUT ON A LIMB

AGAWAM AND WESTFIELD | 2010

It was a hot August morning in 2010 when I walked through the security check point and metal detector in the Westfield District Court. This district court serves several towns, including Agawam where I lived and committed the crime that brought me here. The court hears criminal, housing, juvenile, mental health and other types of cases.

I arrived at 8:30 am and waited in the lobby until the session in Court Room One was scheduled to begin at 9:00 a.m. I knew some of the others waiting for their cases to be called, some of them a few years younger and several senior citizens. I had appeared here in April shortly after I was arrested. At that time, I was given this date to appear before the judge and make my plea.

Some of the defendants went into one of the conference rooms to meet with their attorneys. A few people stepped outside for a smoke while waiting. Several people went directly into the probation office adjacent to the lobby to check in first. A court officer announced that we could all enter the court room. Most of the people seemed to have an attorney and I began to worry since I did not have one and I may not be prepared.

Inside after we all sat down, the court officer announced that all cell phones needed to be turned off and no cameras or recording devices were allowed. The basic pine wooden benches were hard and not upholstered, probably to make sure everyone stayed alert and awake. The clerks and the officers were busy checking their files and preparing for the session. It was a dignified setting with the judge's bench set up on the dais, flanked by the U.S. flag on the left and the Massachusetts flag on the right of the judge's chair. The seal of the Commonwealth was hanging in the center of the wall next to two bookcases filled with lawbooks.

The officers announced the entrance of the judge and we were all asked to stand. He came in and sat down in his chair and we all sat back down. Cases were called by name and number. The defense attorneys sat on the right side and the prosecuting attorneys sat of the left side facing the judge with their backs to the audience.

This morning I watched and listened to each case. Two brothers were present and reported that they had settled their differences with the help of lawyers and their case was dismissed. Another defendant accepted the evidence against her by the prosecuting attorney and pled guilty. Another person described the reasons for not following several conditions of his probation. He was informed by the judge that any further criminal acts or failure to follow the judge's terms would bring him back and result in immediate incarceration. Three other cases were postponed as key witnesses or representatives were absent to testify. Several defendants responded to the judge's questions through the glass windows at the side of the courtroom as they were in one of the locked cells. Several cases were postponed at the first call and the attorney requested a second call until later in the session when an essential person would then be present.

Finally, just before noon, my name and case number were announced by the clerk. I was asked to come to the microphone before the judge. I was asked to raise my right hand and swear that I would be telling the truth.

After the judge looked at the file folder, he asked me, "What is your name?"

"David Sawyer. Sir."

"Are you representing yourself?"

"Yes, sir."

"Were you informed of your right to have an attorney?"

"Yes, sir."

"What is your age?"

"Twenty-six."

"How much education do you have?"

"I graduated from Agawam High School."

"Your file indicates you have waived your right to a trial by a jury of your peers. Do you understand that by that action you also lose several other rights and that the decisions by a judge are final?"

"Yes, your honor, I do understand."

"At this time, are you on any alcohol or drugs or prescription drugs."

"No, sir."

"Do you have any physical or medical condition that could affect your ability to understand or make decisions?"

"No, sir."

The judge continued, "The officer's report states that you were arrested in April 2010 for trespassing and malicious destruction of property. Describe to the court what happened."

"I drove my ATV onto the Christmas tree farm in Feeding Hills after midnight, and cut down a tree."

"A tree? This report states that six full grown Christmas trees, each about ten feet tall, were cut down. Is that correct?"

"Yes", I replied softly.

Looking sternly at me, the judge said, "Based on the value of a tree, the difference between one tree and six trees is a large amount, although either is still a misdemeanor. What did you do after you cut down the trees?"

"I don't remember for sure. I think I left them all there and then drove home."

"Why don't you remember?"

Lowering my head, I answered, "I was drunk."

"Do you believe you would have done this if you were not drunk?"

"No, sir."

"I see that you have several prior arrests and convictions involving other incidents when you were drinking. Although that is not part of this case, it shows a pattern of behavior. Since you were not arrested at the time of the deed, your state of sobriety is not considered part of this action. You need to enter rehabilitation and learn how alcohol has affected your life. Your file indicates that following some of these prior convictions you were required to attend a rehabilitation program. Did you complete those programs?"

I answered, "I attended rehab a few times and I stopped drinking for a while. But I cannot honestly stand here and tell you I am staying sober."

He replied, "As I said, I will encourage you to keep trying to work on your alcohol addiction since that is clearly a part of your repeat offenses. Are you getting that message?"

"Yes, I am, sir. I am ready to volunteer to enter immediately a detox and rehab program."

"I support your decision and hope you will complete this next program. I am going out on a limb here to support your decision. You were sober when you turned yourself into the police. It is a fact that you left the trees there, which avoided a charge of theft. And why did you come onto this property in the first place?"

"I was angry and upset," I said.

"Did you know the owner of the property or have something against her?"

"No. I did not know her and had nothing personal against her. But I knew that the trees were out of sight of her house and the nearest neighbors. It was dark. I figured that no one would see me."

The judge continued, "Let me give you some history of the place. The owner and her husband began their Christmas Tree farm many years ago. It was, and is, an important source of income for them. When her husband died a few years ago, it became even more important as income for her. The farm also improved the property and the neighborhood. It takes many years of care and attention to bring trees to the size that they can be harvested for the Christmas season. Your destruction prevented the trees from being sold. There is no use for cut trees of this type in the summer. Your act also prevented the trees being enjoyed by the families who would have bought them in December."

"I was not thinking of all that."

"Of course, you weren't. Did you act alone? Had you planned to cut down these trees?"

I answered, "Yes. I went alone. I didn't tell anyone what I was going to do. I must have planned to cut the trees, because I went during the middle of the night. And I took my chain saw. There is a dirt bike trail along her land and it is often noisy, so I thought no one would notice the noise from the saw, thinking it might be a dirt bike or ATV."

The judge declared, "I see that it was a few days before your activity was reported. Some of your friends forwarded to the police some pictures you sent them on your cell phone showing the damage that you had done. These included views of your ATV. These pictures are placed as evidence in your file. You incriminated yourself. Was that smart to photograph your own criminal activity and send it onto the internet?"

"No, I guess not. But I didn't show my face."

"You didn't need to show your face. You showed your chain saw, your vehicle and sent the pictures from your smartphone. Not too smart, Mr. Sawyer."

"Duh! No. Not too smart."

He responded, "That is right. You need to think always what you post or allow to be sent. You understand there is no dispute that you committed this misdemeanor? Do you accept responsibility for what you have done?"

"Yes, your honor."

"I declare that you have committed eight counts of malicious destruction of property, and one count of trespassing. How do you plea? Guilty or not guilty?"

Again, in a soft voice, I replied, "Guilty, sir."

"I am able to give your sentence at this time, rather than wait for another date. This court sentences you to fifty hours of community service. You must also pay back to the property owner the value of the destroyed trees. And you have fees to pay to the court. You are placed on six months of probation and due back in this court six months from today. I remind you that if you commit any other crimes or do not keep the terms of your probation I can place you directly into jail. Best wishes, Mr. Sawyer. Next case please."

Relieved with this decision, although embarrassed in front of the audience, I walked out of the court room with a slight nod to some of my friends, but not a trace of a smile. Back in my car, I declared: "Wow! Yes!"

* * *

With the help of my supervisor at H.P. Hood in Agawam and their employee benefits program, and this most recent court appearance before a judge, I voluntarily agreed to enter a twenty-eight day residential detox and rehab program in western New England. Over the next several weeks, I waited until a bed was available. I saved money from my job, and paid to the victim of my crime the cost of the trees that I had destroyed. I also stayed out of trouble and went to AA meetings several nights each week. Soon, summer was over and the leaves were falling off the trees.

Once I began at the rehab center, I made many new friends, each one working to recover from his own addiction. I was twenty-six, among men who ranged from about twenty-two into their sixties. I listened and learned finally, with a willing and honest approach, about the disease of alcoholism. I listened to the staff members who were also counselors teach about alcoholism and its consequences.

Every day had its routine schedule filled with different events to help all of us get better and stay sober. I learned about the twelve steps. During each day's twelve step meeting, we repeated the steps. But our daily work was mostly on the first four steps. Each of those who were ready to complete their program read his personal story to all of us in one of our group meetings.

Here is some of my story which I read to the group at the end of my month:

My first drinks of alcohol began at home at family events or when I was home alone. Both of my parents drank and there was always liquor available. I could sneak drinks from bottles in the refrigerator or in the pantry closet. I enjoyed the taste and the relaxed feeling from the alcohol. After school when I was fifteen, I recall my first drinks, either by myself or with classmates. Usually, we needed someone older to buy alcohol legally and who would supply us. Other times we stole the alcohol.

I barely managed to graduate from Agawam High School because I often skipped some classes during the day or sometimes skipped coming to school the whole day. My attendance record was poor. My participation in classes was poor since I rarely paid attention in class or did my homework. I did graduate with my class but don't remember much after the graduation ceremonies due to drinking with my classmates. We were free from school, although some of them had plans for future studies. I was content to find a job and stay in Agawam.

When I was twenty, my parents moved to South Carolina. They told me they needed to start a new life without being responsible for me. Moving away was their path to getting better. I wanted to stay in Agawam where my friends still lived and worked. I damaged my relationship with my parents by my drinking. At first, I blamed them for abandoning me, but I came to realize I had to take responsibility for my behavior. They had to make decisions for their own health and welfare. For awhile I stayed at the homes of different friends, usually drinking buddies.

My first few jobs ended in getting disciplined, warnings and eventually fired because I was late for work or drunk on the job. Usually these firings were within the first three months of employment, so I was left without a job and had to look again. At the start of each job I started out trying to be responsible and careful, but lost my job each time as the result of my drinking problem.

A couple of my favorite jobs were bussing tables at a restaurant and bar. I often came to work drunk or by sipping during the shift and getting drunk during my work time. I learned from my past mistakes and new ways to stay employed longer. But still managed to keep drinking. I would take the half-filled bottles and cans out to the back and pour them into a gallon container mixed together and stashed behind the dumpster. Part of my work was to put empty bottles into the recycling bin, but I learned to empty bottles for my own consumption. When I finished my shift, I would take the full gallon container to drink off the premises, usually driving home first and then drinking until I fell asleep.

My friends told me I never got angry or violent when drinking, that usually I was first happy and talkative, then quiet and fell asleep. One of my buddies who didn't drink still attended our parties. I asked him "Why don't you drink with us?" He said, "It is more fun to be awake and alert and watch how everyone else behaves when drinking. In the morning I can remember everything and not have a hangover. And you guys would not remember anything and be sick."

I dated one girl for a few years after high school. I moved into her place and I had a place to sleep and eat. For the first several months we got along very well, but then I stopped helping her with our expenses. But after two years of my drinking she gave me an ultimatum "Get out and get sober. I might consider being with you after that. Keep drinking and you can forget about our future together." She emphasized the many times I had promised to do things with her, but then failed to keep my promises. These issues ended our relationship.

After a period of staying with some of my buddies, I was able to buy a used car. I also bought a used mobile home in the Agawam Mobile Home Park on Springfield Street in Agawam. Finally, I was able to take care of my home and transportation. As years went by our former group of friends broke up, as life, work and studies took us in different directions.

One of my best buddies died when he crashed his motorcycle while driving drunk and without wearing his helmet. That was a very difficult time for me and was one big wake-up call to get my life in order. Although I tried to forget my pain and loss by drinking, I began to realize that more alcohol was part of the problem and not part of the answer.

Working at HP Hood I liked the maintenance job but had some arguments with the manager about my work habits. He gave me several opportunities to improve my performance. The incident at the Christmas tree farm occurred while I was working with them. It was ironic that working at a company that produced and distributed milk and other dairy products led me to stop drinking alcohol. After the completion of my most recent recovery program, I went back to work in my entry-level job with HP Hood full time. I continued to drive my car and live in my mobile home at the park in Agawam.

I left the program having made several new friends and continued to attend the AA meetings where I had other new friends, a new sponsor and tools to deal with all of life. This time I avoided any drinking and worked to stay sober.

* * *

In early December, after my August court date and my month in rehab, I began my community service for Mrs. Emily, the tree owner, volunteering part time evenings and weekends at her Christmas tree farm. There were bright holiday lights strung over the entrance. There were also some precut trees and some trees in their root balls in large pots. A large wooden sign visible from the road advertised: **"Christmas Trees for Sale"**.

It was a cold evening and I was dressed in black jeans, boots and a heavy parka. With work gloves on my hands, I was prepared to handle the trees.

Mrs. Emily and I stood in front of the cut and potted trees.

She said, "I am going out on a limb for you. I told the judge and the clerk of the court that I was willing to supervise you while you perform your community service. During this month, you will sell trees to my customers, help them make their selections, cut down trees, and learn firsthand about this business."

I told her, "Mrs. Emily, I am grateful for this opportunity to make amends to you."

She replied, "I was angry at first with you, but realized in the past couple of months that it would be better for me to show you how you can become a better person."

I said, "My intent was not malicious towards you or your trees. I was not thinking of the consequences. I was drinking too much. I was bored."

She asked, "How can you be bored with so much to do in our area. I want you to look around, look into yourself and consider your talents and skills."

"OK"

She said, "My trees look so good they almost seem artificial and so beautiful they should not be harvested."

"That's true," I said.

Mrs. Emily went on, "I also sell live trees with the roots and ball of earth included so the tree can be replanted after Christmas and live many more years."

"That seems like a good choice."

She said, "The fact that a tree is good one year does not mean it will still be commercially valuable the next year. Sometimes, with continued growth it can lose the perfect qualities and become misshapen."

I asked, "How did you get started with growing trees?"

She said, "It started out as a hobby when the gypsy moth infestation required clearing land on our family land. It took a lot of work clearing the fields, moving the rocks, lots of work each season. One of our neighbors told my husband: "You and God have done a wonderful thing, making this land so beautiful." My husband replied. "Yes, but you should have seen how wild and messy it was when God had the land all to Himself."

Mrs. Emily said, "The best land for growing trees is abandoned pasture, meadow or orchard land which has not been used for several years. The control of undergrowth or brushes is simplified if the evergreen saplings are planted before seeds have spread from other types, like red maple, sumac, bayberry, aspen, gray birch and other bushes. The trees are grown in open sunlight on semi-flat land. Many trees planted at the same time will not all result in Christmas trees- even with same care, from the same stock."

"Aha! How fast do they grow?"

She answered, "How fast trees grow depends on the amount of rain, sunlight and fertile soil. The white pine normally grows 10- 12 inches each year, with TLC. The balsam and pine sprouts grow to living room size in about sixteen years. During the year you have to repeat spraying, trimming, liming, fertilizing and cutting the grass and brush. "

"Amazing! And what make a good finished product, Mrs. Emily?"

She replied, "First the year-round maintenance is needed to prepare for the sales which occur from the end of November to the end of December. The goal is the ideal tree- a symmetrical conical shape or taper, long, soft fresh needles, density or so many branches the trunk of the tree cannot be seen, and a bright green color."

"Hmmm!"

Mrs. Emily said, "Some of the factors that can ruin or destroy a crop include insects, rabbits, deer, bacterial or viral disease, lack of rain or too much rain, and in winter freezing that can break limbs. Speaking of disease. How is your rehab going?"

I said, "Fairly well. One day at a time. There is a fact about addiction. It takes time. It takes time to become addicted and time to recover. The program taught me that if you have taken years walking into the forest, or following the addiction, it takes years to get out of the forest."

"Good point."

"I am learning to stop hanging around with those who are sick, people who are negative, or who continue to be addicted. This means making new friends, many of whom are in recovery and those who understand how to live with positive purpose."

She turned towards the road, and announced to me, "Here come some customers. They are all yours."

I smiled and welcomed them, "May I help you? You already picked out and tagged your tree? Is it marked in the field? Would you like me to cut it for you, or do you want to cut it yourselves? That would be fine. Here is a saw. You know where it is? Great. Have fun."

Turning towards her, I asked, "Mrs. Emily, how did you and your husband get into this business?"

"When we were first married, the IRS decided that land used to grow Christmas trees is forest property and that only 50 per cent of the income derived is taxable. We were able to transform some of our idle land and plant the new young trees."

"And how much work year-round do you do?"

"Many people assume that it requires little attention and investment by the grower between planting and harvesting. But growing Christmas trees is a serious year-round commercial enterprise."

I said, "But the final benefits are pretty awesome."

She replied, "Well, they are limited in time. The grower has about

2-3 years when it is best to cut a tree. Christmas trees mature in a short time, compared to other forest crops. They must be cut just before the time of sale, not months ago in the summer."

"Yes, I am really sorry Mrs. Emily that I did that last August. I am doing my best to make up for my mistakes. What can you do with trees that don't sell in their prime years?"

Mrs. Emily said, "If trees grow beyond harvesting for Christmas trees, they can be sold for posts, poles, piling or timber. The growth of unsold trees which are kept to grow will help to protect the watershed and as a buffer to other development. Now here comes another customer. You are on your own to help them buy a tree."

Again, I welcomed the next customer, "Hi there. All of our trees are fresh. You have a choice, between one that is precut or to come out with me and select a tree that I will cut for you. We also have a few trees grown in root balls that you can plant outside after Christmas."

I continued, "To check for freshness among the precut ones, try to bend a few needles. If they feel rubbery and don't break the tree is fresh. You like this one? Mrs. Emily will take your payment. Let me tie it up and put it in your truck."

I set the tree down and wrapped it with rope to keep its branches tight. Then I placed it in the back of the pickup and tied it down.

I said, "Let me give you some advice about the care of your tree. Since it is already cut, you should keep it in a stand with about a gallon of water. Before you put it in its base, slice an extra piece off the bottom of the trunk so it will absorb water better."

I waved to them as they drove away, "Thanks. And Merry Christmas!"

When I returned to Mrs. Emily, she said, "Well, David, you've been doing well today helping our visitors. I will go out on another limb. If you do well this month doing your community service time, and you continue on your path of recovery and rehab, I will consider offering you a part time job in the spring clearing the land and looking after the trees. And I would encourage you to keep working for HP Hood full-time with benefits for the long-term, either here in Agawam or in their warehouse in Suffield."

Smiling, I told her, "Great! That would be wonderful, Mrs. Emily. I am thankful for your trust in me and giving me a second chance."

She answered, "So keep walking out of the forest. You may end up working in a different kind of forest." I hugged her and looked down the road for the next customers.

SEEING RED

WILBRAHAM | 2010

About four weeks before Christmas, I slowly walked up the long front walk of the Wilbraham United Church. A young man was shoveling the front walk which was almost completely clear of snow. There was about six inches of fresh snow on the ground but the temperature was above freezing. He was blond with a small moustache, short and muscular. He had a bright red wool cap and a heavy gray parka coat, blue jeans and tan work boots. He was humming the tune of "White Christmas".

I thought that this is not my lucky day! Things can't get much worse…I'd better be careful what I say. The last time I said that, they did get worse…much worse. I looked around furtively. I never, never thought I would be coming to a church for help!

The young man turned towards me and said, "Hi! I'm Tommy. My real name is Thomas Cranwell, but everyone calls me Tommy. What's your name?"

I replied, "I'm Miguel Perez. I'm glad to meet you. Do you work here?"

"Yes. I'm the janitor for the church. I've almost finished shoveling the walk. Do you like it?"

I said, "Yes, sir. You do good work. But, tell me, why are you so happy today?"

Tommy said, "I'm happy most days. Except on days when I'm not happy. But today, I'm happy. I have a job. I like working. Miguel, do you like your work?"

"If I was working again, I guess I'd be happy too. When I was working I wished I had more free time. Now I have a lot of free time and I wish I was working."

Tommy said, "How come?"

I said, "How come what?"

He said, "How come you don't have a job?"

"I was laid off three months ago from the plant in Springfield, along with fifty other employees. There was not enough work to keep us busy. My bills are piling up since I still have to eat and pay rent. Well, you don't need to listen to my problems."

Tommy smiled, "Sure I do. That's part of my job." I asked, "A janitor listens to problems?"

"Well, it's my job as a Christian, a member of this church. We're here to help one another. Besides, I like listening to people."

I said, "Well, that's thoughtful. Really, though. I need to see if there is someone who can help with my current problem. Is there anybody inside?"

"Yes, Florence, the secretary. She can help you. See you later."

"Thanks. Keep doing your good work. Both the shoveling and the listening."

"Take care." Tommy smiled again and resumed shoveling. I looked at the front door, hesitated, looked around, then went into the building.

I entered the church office and the secretary greeted me: "Good morning. May I help you."

"I hope so. My car ran out of gas. The service station down the street is closed. Do you know when it opens?"

She said, "Usually a half hour after the owner arrives there."

I replied, "Well, it's already ten."

"He must be late today. Or maybe he's sick."

I said, "I'm afraid that won't help me. There are no other gas stations in the area."

She explained, "He has had a difficult time keeping good help. Actually keeping any help at all. Most young job hunters want to get top pay for as little work as possible. Or some potential workers can't be trusted."

"Yeh. That's too bad about the quality of many workers these days."

"Of course, each of us can only be responsible for our own life and how we serve others. I always try to be a good example towards other people. I can even help you with your need for gasoline."

I asked, "Really? How?"

She pointed to the stairway, "In the basement there is a full can of gas. You can use that."

"But you don't even know me. I'm a total stranger. Why should you trust me?"

She extended her hand and shook my hand, "My name is Florence Higgins."

I responded, "And I'm Miguel. Miguel Perez."

"Now we are no longer strangers. I will trust you to bring back the empty can."

The telephone rang, and Florence answered the call. "Excuse me... Good morning, Wilbraham United Church. How are you Mrs. Upjohn...Oh I'm very sorry to hear that... I will be sure to tell Rev. Taylor when she arrives. Please let your family know that we are thinking of all of you. Rev. Taylor will call you as soon as she can. Bye."

She turned to me and said, "The gas can is down the stairs there. You'll see it at the bottom to the right."

"Thank you." I went down the stairs. When I came back up, the secretary was talking on the phone again: "Good morning, Wilbraham United Church. Yes, we do...Our Sunday service is at ten o'clock. This Sunday begins the Advent season and there will be special choir music. I hope that you can come... Well, I'm glad that you found us too.... We are a friendly church. Thanks for calling. Goodbye."

I said to Florence, "Thanks for the gasoline. I'll be right back."

In a few minutes, I returned walking up the front walk swinging the empty gasoline can and passed Tommy, who said, "Well, speak of the devil."

"Excuse me? I may not be such a great person. But I assure you, Tommy, I am not the devil."

Tommy said, "Sorry. Just a figure of speech." I went inside and entered the office, placing the empty container on the floor.

After a few moments, another woman entered from the back door. She took off her coat and scarf, placed them on a hook in the hallway. She was probably in her forties, wearing glasses and her long dark brown hair curled around her neck. She wore a blue sweater and gray pants and black knee-high boots.

She entered the office and declared, "Hi, Florence. How is it going?"

"Busy as usual, Rev. Taylor. You have a few messages. The Women's Fellowship wants you to stop by and say a few words at their meeting next week. And your husband called to say that Henry is sick, not really serious, but that he needs to be picked up from school as soon as possible. Your husband can't get away from his job this morning and your neighbor is away today."

The pastor replied, "No problem. But I will make a few phone calls first. I can leave Henry with my mother. She is visiting us this week."

"Oh. Mrs. Upjohn called a few minutes ago. Her husband has been taken to the hospital with a possible heart attack. She is with him in the waiting room at Mercy Medical Center."

"That's too bad. He had just retired and has been looking forward to this holiday season. I'll go see him as soon as I take Henry home from school."

Tommy entered from the front entrance, after pausing to look back and admire his work. He said, "Hi, Rev. Taylor. I finished the shoveling. Do you want to see it?"

"You did very well. I saw it when I came in from the back. Thanks a lot."

He asked, "Is there anything special you need me to do today?"

She answered, "Well, yes there is. The outdoor manger scene needs to be set up. Maybe tomorrow we can find someone to help you. Who can we get to come over during the day?"

The secretary said, "Reverend Taylor, I would like you to meet Miguel."

"Hi, it is a pleasure to meet you. I am Miguel Perez, unemployed carpenter."

"Maybe you can help us."

"I'm the one who needs to be helped... What can I do to help you?"

The pastor replied, "I've asked Tommy to think of someone who can help set up the outdoor creche tomorrow. Today each of the figures need to be checked to see if any repairs need to be made since last year. Could you do that?"

"Certainly. I've got plenty of time on my hands."

"Tommy can show you what to do in the basement. I have to get on with my work."

Tommy looked at me and said, "Follow me, Miguel. And bring your can."

"I beg your pardon."

"I mean bring your gas can. Another figure of speech."

While Rev. Taylor went into her office, Florence resumed work at her desk. Tommy and I went downstairs to work on the possible repairs. It took several hours but we were able to fix each large life-size wooden figure of the manger scene that was in need of work.

On the afternoon of the next day, Tommy and I brought up the seven large wooden figures of the manger scene. We erected each one in its place on the front yard. While we were carrying one of the Wise Men, Tommy exclaimed, "I'm glad we are almost done. This is heavy work. I never could have done it without you. All we had to do was ask for help and you appeared. An answer to our prayers."

I said, "I'm no answer to someone's prayers. I don't believe in prayer, nor in God."

Tommy replied, "Oh, come on. Everyone believes in God. God is good and God is great."

"Well, I don't. I take care of myself. I don't need someone else to guide my life. Besides, if there is a God, He wouldn't have let all the bad things happen in my life."

"You sure sound angry."

"I am angry. You would be too if you were in my shoes. I can't afford to drive my car. Even if I could drive it, I don't have anywhere I can go. I'm angry because God let me lose my job after six years of hard work there."

"Now I see what makes you so angry."

I said, "Besides all that, this summer my sister was killed in a car accident near our family home in San Antonio, Texas, leaving behind her three small children and her husband. I can't even afford to buy them Christmas presents or go down to visit them this year."

Tommy said, "You do have a lot of problems. But God can help you with one of those you mentioned. He helps me with my problems. I am always grateful for being able to do things in return for His loving care."

"There you go again. So happy and grateful. And you have so little."

"No, really I have a lot. I am healthy. I have a job that I like. I have some friends. I have an apartment. Maybe I'm happy because I accept what I have."

"What do you mean?"

He said, "I am satisfied with what I have, instead of looking at what I don't have."

"You're pretty smart."

"I just try to be me. And not someone I can't be. I think slowly. I can't read very well. But I can be me. And I don't charge for giving advice."

"You are a good man, Tommy."

"So are you, Miguel. I like you."

I asked, "Do you think that this shepherd looks better here? Or, over there?" I pointed to two different locations.

Tommy said, "Well, let's try that spot." We moved the shepherd and secured its base to the ground.

"What do you like about your job here?" I asked.

"First, I get paid. My disability check pays for my rent and food. My job pays for everything else I need. When I lived in the group home, I didn't make as much as when I live on my own."

"What kind of work did you do before here?"

"Well… I've washed dishes, raked leaves, shoveled snow, and mopped floors. But they were always just odd jobs working for different people. Here at the church I work for only one employer and have a steady income as janitor. Right?"

"That's right."

"Have you ever lost any job?"

Tommy answered, "Yes. I lost some jobs because I get nervous around lots of people. Also, some of my bosses wanted me to work faster than I could. I hate being rushed."

"It must be better now that you are working here."

"Here I am around people I like because they accept me as I am. They don't make fun of me. Florence and Rev. Taylor are very kind and caring when they ask me to do the work."

I said, "I know it is important to have an understanding boss. I've had bad luck with some of my supervisors. I always think I know more than they do."

Tommy raised his hand and pointed his finger at me, "That's not good. Even if you do know more than the boss you shouldn't tell her that you do."

"Actually, that is the main reason I lost my last job. If I had kept my mouth shut and done my work quietly I'd probably still be there. Some of the other carpenters were not laid off."

"I thought you said that God made you lose your job."

"You're right. I did say that. But, I guess it was partly my responsibility, plus the circumstances of the job."

"Well, you shouldn't be blaming God for losing your job. He gets blamed enough for everything as it is. Like floods, tornadoes and earthquakes."

"O.K., Tommy. I will stop blaming God and accept my part in the problem."

"I'm sure He will be happy with that."

As I started to set up another figure, I asked, "Can you help me with this one?"

Tommy replied, "Sure. I once heard this saying: "My life is God's gift to me. What I do with my life is my gift to God." God blessed me with being alive. The rest is up to me."

"But what if I don't believe in God."

"Well, you just said you would stop blaming God for the loss of your job. I think that you are mixed up about what you do believe."

"Why do I have so many problems in my life if there really is a God?"

"Rev. Taylor says "God never promised us that we would have no problems. He promised us the power and guidance to solve our problems. It is our job to solve them, with His help."

"For someone so simple, you have a lot of wisdom."

"Simple? I think that was a compliment. Thank you."

"Yes, I mean being simple isn't a weakness. It is a strength."

Tommy said, "Having trust in God is a strength. That is simple. It works for me."

I said, "Here, let's move this one over here near the manger." We then moved Joseph closer to Mary.

"You know, Joseph was a carpenter too. He taught his son how to make things out of wood, You, Joseph and Jesus all have the same jobs."

"That's right. I never thought of that. Hey, if we all belong to the same union, maybe Joseph and Jesus can help me find a new job."

"Well, it can't hurt to ask."

I looked into the face of Joseph and asked, "Hi there, Joseph, could you do me a favor?"

Tommy said, "That's the way."

I continued, looking into his dark brown eyes surrounded by his black eyebrows, moustache and beard. "Joseph, could you help me find a good job, using my carpenter skills? I'd even settle for a good job doing anything."

Tommy responded, "There now. You asked for help. Maybe God can help you with your anger."

"What does God have to do with this? I'm talking to Joseph."

He said, "Well, God works through all sorts of people, living and dead. So let Him help you with your anger."

I shouted back, "What anger?"

"That anger! You can give it over to Joseph, or to God. Just let it out."

I said, "If I get angry at God, and there really is a God, won't I get punished? Won't He get angry at me?"

He countered, "Even if He does, it will probably be good for Him too. But I believe that God is loving. He is able to accept all your anger, as long as you accept the fact that you have a right to be angry. After that, maybe you can see more clearly to act on your own life. And stop blaming God and others for your problems."

"Who's blaming God?"

"There you go again. Just tell Joseph how you feel."

Turning back looking into Joseph's face, I said, "Hey Joseph. I am angry about a lot of things. I need you to help me get it all out. Will you accept my anger without getting mad at me?" I looked at Tommy and said, "He smiled at me! Joseph smiled at me. I don't believe it... Yes, I do."

Tommy said, "O.K. I believe you. I knew he'd be a good listener."

"But I still feel angry."

He said, "What do you expect? Instant miracles?"

I answered, "I guess I am still upset because I want more than I have. I expect life to be without any problems."

Tommy asked, "Do you want me to show you the only people I know who don't have any problems?"

"Sure."

Tommy pointed to the area beyond a row of trees, "Right over there."

"But that's a cemetery. Everyone is dead there."

"Right. But they don't have any problems. They don't even have to worry about lawn care. Perpetual care, you know."

I asked, "So what's your point?"

Instantly Tommy responded, "As long as you have problems, it means you are still alive."

I said, "That is logical. Well, to get back to my problem. What good is a car if I can't keep it running. I have to pay registration, insurance and taxes even if the car doesn't go anywhere."

Tommy said, "Why can't you use it to drive people around on errands. People who will pay for your services."

"You mean be a taxi driver?"

He said, "Sort of. It beats sitting around and complaining about your life. You can use your car, charge enough to pay for expenses and some extra. You'll also keep busy."

"But I'd rather be doing carpentry work."

"I'm not saying do this the rest of your life. Just long enough until you get the job you want. There must be some people who need rides and can afford to pay a driver."

I said, "That's a grand idea. I'll bet Florence or Rev. Taylor can suggest some possible customers among the church members. I'll have to ask them about it."

Tommy said, "Well, we still have to get some hay for the stable"

"What do you mean? That's your job."

He said, "But I don't have a car."

Smiling, I said, "How much will you pay for a ride?"

"Miguel, that's not fair."

"Only kidding! I'm only kidding. I can get some hay in the next few days. We don't want to put it down until the snow melts some more."

"This was a good day's work."

I agreed, "I have to admit I feel a lot better having done something constructive today."

"You made my work easier too. It would have been impossible for me to set this up without your help."

"You could have done it with anyone."

"You are the one who was meant to come today to help me put this up."

I stated, "In exchange I got some gas for my car, plus some free advice."

Tommy asked, "What are you going to do about the missing manger? We still need a crib to hold the baby Jesus."

I replied "I can make a new one at home. I've got the lumber and the tools."

Tommy asked, "Will you be coming back then?"

I said, "Yes, I'll bring the new manger back in a couple of days. But I need to go now."

Tommy and I shook hands. "See you later. Bye."

As I walked down the sidewalk, I said, "Bye, Tommy. Bye, Joseph. Thanks." To myself, I thought, I know that Joseph smiled at me.

Tommy looked at the statue of Joseph and smiled broadly.

Two weeks later, the week before Christmas.

As I walked up towards the church, I thought to myself: "Here I am again. I never thought I'd be having an appointment to talk with a pastor."

Florence greeted me when I came into the office, "Hi there, Miguel. How have you been? I haven't seen you around for a few days. Have you been all right?"

Shaking my head side to side, I said, "I guess if everything was all right I wouldn't need an appointment."

She reported, "I know that Rev. Taylor is looking forward to meeting with you. She should be helpful."

"That's good. How is Tommy? We went to the movies last week, but I haven't talked with him in a couple of days."

She answered, "He's well. Right now, he's caroling with the church choir. They've gone to the nursing home to visit some of our resident members. He loves to sing with the choir. Everyone enjoys caroling, giving and receiving the joy of music."

I told her, "Please tell him I said "Hi". He is a good person. "

She picked up the phone, "Good afternoon. This is Wilbraham United Church… Oh certainly. You can still order a poinsettia plant for Christmas Eve… How do you want your gift to be listed in the bulletin?" She wrote down the message while listening. "That will be lovely. After the service Christmas Eve you can either take your plant home with you, or you can donate it to one of our at home members or hospitalized members. Which would you prefer? O.K. That will be much appreciated… Is your daughter coming home for the holidays?... Great… See you next Sunday in church. Good bye."

I told Florence, "I almost forgot. I'd like to order two poinsettia plants myself for Christmas Eve. The first one can be given in memory of my sister, Gloria Sanchez, by her brother, Miguel Perez. The second one, in memory of my mother, Maria Perez, by her son, Miguel."

Florence asked, "Will you take them home, or do you want to donate them?"

I paused and then answered, "I'll take one to keep. The other one can be given to Mr. and Mrs. Upjohn. Do you know where poinsettias came from?"

She answered, "From the florist."

"Well. Yes. But I mean where in the world do they come from?"

"I don't know."

I continued, "Poinsettias were first brought to the United States from Mexico, my ancestral country."

"Really?"

"They are a native plant of southern Mexico. They were first brought to the United States by a former American ambassador to Mexico, Joel Poinsett. The people there called them 'the flower of the Holy Night.' "

She asked me, "Did you grow up in Mexico?"

"No, I am a fourth generation American. We have lived north and east of the Rio Grande River, above the border, in Texas, in the town of Uvalde, west of San Antonio."

She said, " I never knew about the history of the poinsettia. It is such a beautiful plant. Oh, by the way, did you hear that someone stole the baby Jesus statue from the manger that you made for us outside?"

"Yes, I heard. I can't imagine anyone stealing the little baby Jesus. Maybe it is someone upset against God, so they kidnapped the baby as ransom."

She said, "If the person has a conscience, he must be very uncomfortable."

"I hope that it shows up before Christmas. The day wouldn't seem right with Jesus still missing."

"I agree with that...Let me tell Rev. Taylor that you are ready to see her. Florence got up and knocked on the office door. "Miguel is here to see you."

Rev. Taylor answered, " Send him in, please."

"Go right in."

Rev. Taylor welcomed me with a handshake. "It's good to see you again. Take off your coat... Have a seat."

I hesitated, " I'm not sure why I'm here...But I feel I need to talk with you."

She said, "First, just relax. As you start talking, maybe you will remember why you are here."

I said, "I'm so nervous. I think better if I can walk around."

"Go ahead. Whatever makes you feel at ease. Let me say something first. I hope that you know how much your help around the church has been appreciated by me these past two weeks. I am grateful for the work on repairing the manger scene statues, making the manger, and helping Tommy with some of his work."

I said, "Well it was good for me too."

Rev. Taylor continued, "Many people receive strength and guidance by stopping during the day or in the evening to visit Jesus and His family. They come to reflect about the real meaning of Christmas, and to think about the love and joy that come from God."

I replied, " I know. Several nights I have come myself to visit the manger. I also enjoy listening to the comments of others standing nearby. One father explained to his little son almost the whole story of the birth of Jesus in Bethlehem. He told all about the angels, the shepherds, the wise men. Another time an elderly woman came with her two grandchildren. They were so excited about the little baby being born in the manger."

Rev. Taylor said, "I believe that the outdoor Nativity scene helps people think about their lives and how we can all slow down and pay more attention to the spiritual part of our lives. This season is not about running around in a big rush buying gifts and feeling pressured and hassled by all the shopping and activities. The central meaning is in the gift of God's Son to each of us. Jesus is one who was very much like us and can help us understand the love and mercy of God, His Father."

I said, "I think that is why I am here today. When I first came here early this month, I was upset about God, the church in general, and other people in my life. For example, everyone with the church has welcomed me. But I have had many, many times in the past when someone has told me, "Go back to the country you came from!" I learned to reply to such unwelcoming comments: "I am an American citizen. I was born in San Antonio, Texas, USA., north of the Rio Grande. And my parents were also born in Texas and have always been American citizens. This is the country I come from!"

I blamed others for all problems. Slowly, in the past few days, I have learned that I have been self-centered and self-pitying. I guess I need some help in sorting out my feelings. I need to take some positive action about my future."

She said, "It sounds as if you are already on the right road, going in the right direction. Looking to yourself to find out what you can do."

I said, "I thought I had all the answers. That I was right and deserved some special treatment. One thing that helped has been to stop and visit with Joseph, the statue out front. I talk to him, tell him my troubles, and I believe he listens to me."

She said, "Each of us has different ways that work in our lives. It is important that what you have found is helping you."

I edged over to the chair and sat down. "It is so hard to think about God as some great power who listens to me. But a statue of Joseph, someone like a person, like me, helps. If I can see or touch someone, it becomes real for me."

She said, "I believe each of us is touched by God in different ways. One way, for me, is through the words and lives of other people. For example, you have been a blessing to Mrs. Upjohn. Taking her in your car every day to visit her husband in the hospital has been very important to her. She has told me how much your help has meant to her since she cannot drive."

I said, "It is really the other way around. I am the one who has benefitted from her sharing with me. It has been a pleasure driving her back and forth each day. I've also seen my problems as small compared to her problems. I have seen how much she and her husband care for each other. I have seen how precious life is, and how easily it can be taken away from us."

The pastor said, " You are also generous. She told me that she has offered to pay for the rides. But that you refused, and suggested that she should give the money to the church if she wanted. That was a kind suggestion."

I explained, "My first idea was that I could drive people on errands to earn some money while I am out of work. With Mrs. Upjohn and her limited income I saw it as a mission for me to take her so she could be with her husband without charging her. Besides I receive new strength when I see how they encourage each other."

Rev. Taylor said, "You'll be glad to know that he is coming home soon. Your helping Mrs. Upjohn every day has had a large part in his steady recovery."

I said, "That's good to know. In the meantime, I've been able to earn regular income by transporting other people for a fee. Florence called several people when I first met her. She introduced me to some people who could afford to pay, but needed rides to the store or for errands in town, along with all kinds of appointments."

The pastor declared, "I'm glad that we've been able to help you earn some money."

I said, " When I first came here I was angry at God for causing me to lose my job. But Tommy helped me see that it was not God's fault. He taught me to be grateful for what I still had, instead of being upset about what I had lost."

She said, "It is difficult when we are overwhelmed by problems to see that there is a bright side to life. It is also easier to blame others and develop anger and resentment. It is harder to make the effort to look at our own responsibility in the problem, and then to work at some positive changes."

I said, "I still need some guidance in dealing with my anger. How can I get rid of it?"

Rev. Taylor said, "First, it is necessary that you accept that you are angry. There is nothing wrong with feeling angry. But you need to learn what is making you feel angry, and what you can do about it."

"I am still angry that I lost my job. After six years working I thought my job there was secure....I'm also angry that my sister was killed this summer, with so much to live for. She was so young. Everything was going well in her life. She had a wonderful husband. She had three great children. They are my niece and nephews. In one quick moment, everything was destroyed."

The pastor responded, " I am sorry to hear that. How did she die?"

I responded, "It was not her fault. She was driving by herself near San Antonio. She had the right of way going through an intersection." I began to halter and choke. "The other driver sped right through his red light. She never, never had a chance. I stopped talking and placed my head in my hands. After a pause, I could continue. "She was always a careful driver. She was courteous. She always used her seat belt. But that other guy didn't even slow down... He was so drunk he couldn't even walk straight."

Rev. Taylor offered me a box of tissues. "I am truly sorry. I know it hurts to remember what happened. I can tell you really loved your sister and miss her. Take your time."

I said, "Why does it still hurt so much. Gloria was killed four months ago. I should be getting over it by now. Shouldn't I?"

She continued, "We never get over the death of a close loved one. We learn how to go on with our lives. But we continue to experience the pain and suffering. There is no timetable that you need to follow in your own sorrow. It takes time to heal. You need to give yourself opportunities to remember her, and feel that pain of losing Gloria. You miss her. We don't just forget someone who leaves us. Our love and feelings go on."

I said, "That's for sure. This summer, for the first two months, I couldn't even talk about her. I couldn't cry. I just walked around in a daze. That was the same time when I lost my job." My crying subsided and I paused to gain control.

Rev. Taylor said, " Miguel, that was a natural reaction. You had been dealt terrible blow. You were in shock. That was probably the way your body and your mind helped you deal with the suffering. Now, with the passage of time, you are able to feel and talk about her."

I replied, "She truly lived up to her name. She was filled with glory and praise. She was radiant and positive. She loved God and was active in her church in Texas. But I can't be like her. I am still angry. What can I do about that?"

The pastor said, "First, you need to accept that it was not God's fault that she was killed. It was a terrible accident that ended her life. God is a force for life, not for death."

I asked, "Then should I continue to blame the drunk driver? Should I be angry at him?"

She answered, "Certainly. It makes more sense to focus on the real cause of her death. But again, the driver did not intend to kill her. Alcohol had taken over his life and his judgment. I am sure that he has suffered greatly for his actions and that he does not need further blame."

"But I need to do something!"

"Right. You can take this strong feeling and channel it in constructive, positive ways to encourage new life and hope from this tragedy. You can make something good come from something evil."

I asked, "Like what?"

"You can continue to do what you have been doing to help others. There is also another action you can share in this holiday season. It is a nation-wide effort to channel the energy and pain that results from friends and family members who are destroyed. Maybe it can help you too."

"Please go on."

"I have lost several friends in motor vehicle accidents caused by drunken drivers. I have conducted funerals for too many people who were killed by the acts of those on drugs or alcohol. Every time I think about those friends who are no longer with us, or take part in the funeral service for such people, I feel the loss and sadness. It hurts...But I take part in the activities of a group that is working to overcome that grief with specific acts. I support the efforts of M.A.D.D., Mothers Against Drunk Driving."

"What do you do with them?"

She said, "I tie a red ribbon on the left side of my car, on the door handle or on the radio antenna. Every time I get in the car I stop. I think about those who have been killed or seriously injured in traffic accidents. I think about the tragic consequences for the surviving families and friends. I am reminded when I get in my car to drive carefully and to be more alert in my own driving habits."

"That sounds good. I know that I often drive faster during this time of the year, rushing to get places fast. But why do you use a red ribbon? What's so special about red?

She told me, "Miguel, for centuries red has been the color of remembering those who have died. It is the color of the martyrs. It is the color of blood. It is also the festive color of Christmas. Even at the time of celebrating Jesus' birth, we remember that he will be crucified and give his blood for all people."

I said, "The Christmas season is certainly an important time to encourage people to drive more safely. All of the holiday parties and rushing in traffic can lead to accidents. With all the emphasis on joy and families being together for the holidays, it is difficult to hear about and remember people getting hurt or killed."

Rev. Taylor said, "It is sad when people don't value life as a precious gift. But it is even harder, as you say, to deal with death in the midst of the joy of the Christmas season."

"It must be good to see other cars with red ribbons, knowing that other people are remembering other victims."

I see this as a silent fellowship of witnesses, those who suffer loss, who remember those who have died. Also, we are doing something about the future to improve the chances of other people when they are on the road." Rev. Taylor took a red ribbon from her desk drawer and gave it to me. "Here is your ribbon to put on your car. I give this to you in memory of Gloria."

I responded, "Thank you. Now I see one way I can turn my anger into a power for good. It is strange. Just before I came in to see you, I ordered two red poinsettias for Christmas Eve, one of them to remember Gloria. I feel better already, knowing that I am not alone in my sadness. And it is a comfort to share my pain in fellowship with others who also suffer their losses."

The pastor said, "I certainly hope our talk has been helpful. I need to end our visit today. I'll look forward to seeing you again."

" Thanks again."

I got up, put on my coat and left the office. As I was in the hall, I heard Rev. Taylor make a phone call:

"Hi honey. I want you to know I'll be home soon. No meetings tonight so we can have some time together with Henry... I love you... See you soon!"

I stopped at Florence's desk and told her, "Florence, I feel so much better after talking with Rev. Taylor."

Florence replied, "She's good at helping people feel better about their lives. We are so fortunate to have her as our pastor."

I said, "I just couldn't see anything good about my problems. Everything seemed so dark and gloomy."

She said, " Unfortunately, we sometimes need a dark experience in order to appreciate the light in the world. We need to know death personally before we can value life that we often taken for granted." She paused and then asked me, "Did you ever go camping?"

"Sure, lots of times. During my early years when I lived in Texas. Why?"

"When you were out at night, out in the fields or open roads, what did you see when you looked up?"

I said, "The stars of course. If it was a clear night. I remember seeing thousands of twinkling stars. I used to call it the canopy of heaven. When I was a kid, I thought of the stars showing the beauty of God's universe. I haven't looked up in a long time. And I certainly have not thought about God's universe... I could name most of the major constellations: Cassiopeia, Canis Major, Canis Minor, Orion. I'd almost forgotten about the stars."

" Maybe it's time to start remembering and looking again. Can you see those same stars in the daytime?"

I said, "Of course not. The sky is too bright. You can only see stars after dark."

Florence said, " But the stars are there all the time, night or day. It takes the darkness for us to be able to see them in all their glory. I know in the city it is often impossible to see the stars because of the bright city lights. When we are out in the country. We can see and enjoy them. What does this mean to you?"

I said, "That we can see the hope and love of God best when it is darkest in our lives. We only see the stars in the darkness."

Florence continued, "In the same way, we can see hope in contrast to the darkness of suffering in the world. We often take our lives for granted. We need difficult, dark times to help us see the beauty in our lives."

I said, "I guess it also means that if I'm looking down at the ground, I'll never see the beauty of the heavens above... Well, it's getting late. I have to go pick up the ladies who need rides from the senior center. I'm going to put this ribbon on my car right away too. Goodbye!"

She smiled and waved, "Take care. Have a good day!"

As I went outside I stopped at the statute of Joseph and said, " See you later, Joseph…the carpenter."

Christmas Eve

On Christmas Eve I came to the sanctuary for the service and sat in the front row facing the pulpit. Florence and Miguel were seated on each side of me. The Communion table had been decorated with a white cover and candlesticks. Red poinsettia plants had been arranged around the front of the sanctuary. Rev. Taylor was seated behind the pulpit. The organist was playing Christmas carols.

Florence whispered to me " I love Christmas Eve! Everyone is waiting for the coming of the baby Jesus. It is a time to prepare for the day to come."

Tommy agreed, "I love Christmas too. The candles are like stars in the night. The music is so joyful."

Rev. Taylor stood up at the front of the sanctuary. "We welcome each of you as we worship together. We take time from our activities preparing for Christmas Day. One of the ways that we share our faith with the people of our community is with our outdoor Nativity scene. Many people were upset when the baby Jesus disappeared from his manger ten days ago. Many people believed that some disturbed person took the statue as a criminal act or as a prank. More important than the presence of a statue is being aware that God can be born anew in each of our lives."

"Earlier today I learned what really happened to our lost baby Jesus. A little girl who lives in the neighborhood came with her mother to report that she had taken the baby and kept it hidden in her home. She returned it today so that it would be in the manger for Christmas morning. Why did she take the baby?" "My daughter told me, 'I was worried that the baby wrapped only in a little clothing would freeze and get sick. So I took him home with me where I kept him in my room with my dolls. I've kept him warm. I fed him and rocked him to sleep every night.' " " When her mother discovered that the little girl had a secret addition to her collection of dolls, and where it came from, she suggested that her daughter return the baby to our church. The girl had already planned to return Jesus here for Christmas. She also insisted that I take good care of the baby Jesus. The little girl made a place in her heart and in her home to welcome the babe of Bethlehem. In that same spirit, may each of us tonight make room in our hearts and our homes for the true presence of God. May the holy child be born in us today. Let us sing together 'O Little Town of Bethlehem.' "

The congregation stood and sang the carol. Tommy turned to me when the carol was over. " I like that song."

Florence said, "Me too. It is one of my favorite carols."

Rev. Taylor continued her message: " Each of us comes this evening with our needs and our hurts, our joys and our sorrows. Each of us is seeking the peace and love that comes from God. We come to thank God for all our blessings. We are glad tonight to see Mr. and Mrs. Upjohn and thankful for his complete recovery and return home this week." I turned around and waved to them. " There are many stories associated with Christmas Eve. One of them is the legend of the poinsettia. Long ago in Mexico, the crowds in one village hurried to lay their gifts and flowers before the statue of the Virgin Mary and the Christ Child. As the people rushed by to the church, a young woman in tears knelt along the roadside. She was crying because she had no gift to bring to the baby Jesus. She had nothing to give. She was very sad. No one stopped to help her. Her tears fell on the dust-covered weeds at her feet. She wiped away the tears falling down her cheeks, and rose to go back home. Then she looked down at the weeds and saw that her tears had washed away the dust from the leaves, which had turned bright red. She gathered together some of the red leaves, filling her arms with their radiant brightness. She rushed to the church. She laid her offering of the poinsettias as her gift before the Christ child. May the beauty of the poinsettias this evening symbolize your gifts to God. May we remember that our tears of sadness, as we remember those who are no longer with us, reveal the love and mercy of God."

"Now let us sing together 'Angels We Have heard on high'.

As the carol came to a close, I knelt down on the floor in prayer.

Tommy asked, "Are you all right?"

I said, "Yes, Tommy. My Gloria has been given to God in the highest. I am all right."

Rev. Taylor spoke, "In silence, let us reflect what the meaning of God is for us. Let us prepare our hearts to make room for His coming. Make room for God's presence within you. Be filled with his presence." After a pause, she looked up and spoke again. "Our new friend, Miguel Perez, has been helping several of us during the last few weeks. He wishes to say a few words."

I stood up and turned around to face the congregation. Tommy patted me on the shoulder.

I spoke: " First, I want to thank you for being here when I came here as a stranger. I was an angry man who did not believe that God cared for me. In the past few weeks, I have learned a lot about how much God lives among us. I have found new hope for my own life and work. I have met many wonderful people in this church. Some of you have given me jobs to do. Several of you have hired me to work as a carpenter in your homes and offered work for many months to come. I believe that I will be busy as a self-employed carpenter, able to earn money doing what I love doing."

"Even more important, I have come to accept the death of my sister Gloria. I have joined with many of you to share the symbol of the red ribbon as we remember those who have died in accidents caused by drunk drivers. I still miss her very much, but I have learned to accept her death and give myself to a cause greater than myself, to bring new life out of death."

"When Gloria and I were little children living in San Antonio, we had a little manger scene in our home. Every Christmas we would unpack it and place it in our living room. Seeing the large manger scene outside gave me an idea. I came here thinking I had nothing to offer to the Christ Child. But I have made a gift for your church, my church. Tommy, can you help me?" Together we uncovered the new wooden manger scene at the front of the sanctuary. Tonight, I give this manger scene for your church family. I came here a wanderer, a stranger. An American who often was not welcomed by other Americans. You gave me a new family. You helped me to know the love and mercy of God by your love to me. I am able to give back to you and to God. May God bless each of you in all the days ahead."

Rev. Taylor said, "Thank you Miguel for your special Christmas gift. As we prepare to give our offerings, I invite you to come forward and leave your gifts before the Christ Child in the manger as we sing our final carol 'Silent Night, Holy Night'."

At the end of the song, Rev. Taylor lifted up her arms to pronounce the blessing upon the congregation.

"Now may you go forth from this holy place, filled with the blessing and love of God. May the Babe of Bethlehem be born again in your hearts and homes. Go in peace. Amen."

THE CLOWN AND THE ACROBAT

WEST SPRINGFIELD | SEPTEMBER 2011

Among the many events and activities at the Big E each year in West Springfield, one of the biggest attractions is the circus. This is one story about a memorable September 2011 early afternoon performance of the travelling circus troupe under the big tent. As part of the American troupe there were several International performers: acrobats from China, clowns from Romania, horses from Canada, elephants from India, dogs from France. Throughout the Big E grounds and buildings there were foods from every possible ethnic and national background, helping to make this annual gathering an all-American experience, which means a global experience.

It was a perfect sunny and warm day to enjoy all of the features of the Big E. The first of the thousands of visitors were already attending the variety of events in the Better Living Center, the Young Building and the Stroh Building along New England Avenue. After waiting in line, near the giant slide, for the first performance of the day, the crowd moved into the tent. Cotton candy, popcorn and soda vendors sold their products up and down each section of the audience in their seats. After the grand welcome by the circus master, the lights brightened the one ring and the crowd settled down for the upcoming entertainment. The show began with several acts of a juggler and magician, and some small dogs doing their routine of trained skills. The band played musical tunes to accompany each act.

Two roustabouts quickly ran past the couple. Anna reached up and squeezed Paul's big red-rubber nose. He smiled at his young blonde fiancée from beneath his brightly colored smile. As he gazed at her from his blue eyes and pinkish eyelids under bushy green eyebrows, his wrinkles, below a high forehead painted white, indicated that he was perhaps middle-aged. Anna, wearing blue tights and a white satin blouse covered with blue sequins, continued their conversation.

"Dearest, in your act you make the children forget their troubles and fears. They laugh at you. They escape from real life."

"You are forgetting," Paul replied, "that your high wire act is as much an escape from real life as my clown act. You, your father and your brothers, all scare and thrill the crowd with your feats of grace and daring. The children sit at the edge of their seats and watch your amazing acrobatic artistry, meanwhile forgetting their own lives."

"Aber nein!" Anna exclaimed, stamping the ground with her foot to emphasize the negative. "Our Zimmermann family shows the people our courage and skill in the face of great danger. We don't hide behind masks or costumes. We teach the audience how to be proud and fearless. Is that what you call running away from real life?"

After a pause, Paul answered slowly, "While you might not be running away from real life, you are afraid up there."

"Of course, but we must all learn to live with fear."

"From down below, everything looks so easy and simple. The children believe, because of your deceptive calmness, that you are not afraid. Doesn't that teach children to escape from reality, pretending not to be afraid, and deceiving them?"

Anna stated, "I admit that I am afraid when we perform. But we learn to live with such difficulties and control them. We still perform our acts."

"I cannot see the value of risking your life each time."

"Darling, we don't teach the children in the crowd how to be heroes. They must learn for themselves how to live with courage and strength. As a child, I was afraid of the dark until I learned what was really hidden in it. At first, I was afraid to be a trapeze artist with my family. Now, I would not want to do anything else."

Paul said, "Once we are married, my sweet, we will begin a new type of life. Our home, our children, other duties will replace this acrobatic life."

Anna replied, "Surely I can continue with this work, too. Human beings are the only animals, that can think about fears, about life, about death, about destiny. The glory of being human is that we dare to defy death, the end of life."

Paul asked, "Is this why you want to perform the double exchange in mid-air even though your father is not sure that you are ready?"

"Yes, perhaps. Papa wants me to be so careful. I know that I can do it. We have practiced for months so that we are all ready. It is the hardest acrobatic feat that I have learned. It is the fulfillment of my career as an aerialist, as a circus performer."

Suddenly, the band music rose in sharp crescendo, reminding Anna and Paul that it was time to perform their separate circus acts. The equestrian performance was just finished. Reassuringly, Paul squeezed Anna's hand.

"My love, be careful."

"Yes, darling. I'll see you shortly."

Paul walked over to a short brown donkey, tied a few feet away. He untied it. The clown and the donkey trotted merrily onto the arena floor. The clown began chasing the donkey in circles, trying to catch him. The saddled donkey ran into the circle from which the graceful horses had departed moments before. The clown grabbed vainly, trying to mount the animal's back. After a few times around the ring, the clown awkwardly grasped the saddle horn and began swinging his body onto the donkey. Oops! The silly clown sprawled onto the sawdust, the saddle slipped off the donkey and fell on top of him. The children squealed with delight. The adults guffawed with laughter. Slowly, the clown stood up. The donkey came behind him and gave him a butt with his head, sending the clown flat on his stomach. The cymbals clashed. The crowd roared.

Again, the bald white-faced clown picked himself up. He dusted himself off. As he did, the donkey backed up to him, swinging his tail. The clown grabbed the tail and brushed himself more effectively with it. The clown looked up to the top of the big tent. The Zimmermann family had already ascended the tall ladder connected to the tent pole. The band music announced that the next act was to begin high above the crowd. Paul climbed on the donkey's back and they began to leave the circle, with the rider waving to the audience on both sides. The clown reached back and struck the rear flank of the animal. The donkey's rear end dropped abruptly to the ground. The clown was quickly dumped into the sawdust. Again, the audience erupted with laughter. The donkey rose up and scampered out of the arena, with the clown chasing wildly after him.

The large lights now turned towards the high platform. Four people stood poised, two on one platform and the other pair on the opposite platform. Anna stood with her brother Hans, who, at twenty-two, was four years older than his only sister. Across the space stood Heinrich, twenty-eight, with their father, Karl. The middle-aged man had brought his three children from Germany to America three years ago. The Zimmermann family was a name renowned in the circus world for their aerial acrobatics. Karl's parents had begun the family tradition. For the past two years this younger group had toured with the American circus. They had been well known in Europe. They now needed to establish their fame in this new country.

The matinee crowd became very quiet. Uptilted wide eyes watched intently as the figures above prepared for their act. The family sought to please each audience with their abilities. They would perform again that evening for a different crowd. But excellence and excitement was promised and given at every performance. Little mouths sticky with candy hung open with expectation. Wrinkled faces of grandparents viewed the scene with childish pleasure. A child's small hand reached in the dark to find his father's reassuring grasp as the thrilling performance began.

Alone, standing beside the wall of the big tent, Paul watched intently. His eyes focused on a small young woman in blue tights high above.

Hans hooked his legs around the ropes of the trapeze and let his body hang down from the bar. Anna stepped from the platform onto the bar and they began swinging into the airspace. She slipped over him, head first, and he held her by her ankles swinging below him. Then Karl slipped from the platform onto the opposite trapeze bar, hooked his legs around the ropes, and suspended himself from the bar. The two trapezes swung through the air toward each other, coming within twenty feet of each other at the closest point. They were one hundred twenty feet above the ground. There was no net below them. They swung back towards their separate platforms and again headed in two sweeping arcs toward each other.

As Anna and Hans swung toward him, Karl called out the cadence count, assuring their precise timing. The band drums began to beat a steady roll. Karl yelled, "Ein... Zwei...Drei... Yip!" Hans released his grip on Anna's ankles and she sailed perfectly through the air to be grasped by her arms in the hands of her father. The cymbals clashed victoriously. A unanimous sigh of relief was followed by a few seconds of applause. The Zimmermanns swung back to their platforms. The single exchange had been well executed. The face of the clown relaxed. His chest heaved softly.

When Hans swung back to his platform, Heinrich jumped nimbly onto the trapeze bar. While they swung out into the space, Heinrich slipped down over Hans to be held by his legs in the grip of the younger brother's strong hands.

On the other side, as they swung back toward the other platform, Karl asked Anna, hanging below him, "Are you ready to go ahead?" She replied, "Ja, Papa." As they swung out toward the other trapeze bar, Karl nodded to Hans. The two arcs separated once more and then began toward each other again. Heinrich and Anna would be exchanged in a double exchange in mid-air, high above the ground below.

The drums began a steady staccato rhythm. The audience was tense with excitement.

Paul watched constantly from his secluded corner. Karl began the count again, "Ein... Zwei...Drei... Yip!" Karl let go of Anna's ankles. At the same moment, Hans released Heinrich. The two persons sailed through the air crossing in flight. Karl grabbed Heinrich's arms and made the grip tighten. In a split second, the cymbals clashed anticipating the grab towards Anna. But Hans could not stretch to reach Anna's hands. Without a scream, her body plummeted swiftly to the ground. The double exchange had failed in tragedy.

The entire crowd gasped in horror. The crowd rose to its feet. Paul rushed over to Anna's crumpled body, reaching her just before the other performers and crew gathered around her. The arena lights were turned up brightly. Paul knelt beside the still, small figure. Karl, Hans and Heinrich quickly descended down the ladders and pushed through the small group, their eyes trembling. One man calmly felt for a pulse, but found no sign of life. The circus crew formed a circle around her body shielding the audience, especially the children, from viewing the scene.

Curled on her side, she rested in a grotesque manner. Eyes closed, her mouth hung open. Bright red blood oozed from her mouth and mingled with the sawdust beneath her shoulder. The clown, tears streaking down his makeup, shaking in agony, cradled her body in his arms. Karl and her brothers crouched over her, mute and dazed, staring at her arms and legs, hoping for some movement. But there was no motion, no signs of life.

Within minutes the West Springfield ambulance drove into the center of the arena floor. The crowd around her was pushed back as the EMTs jumped out and lifted Anna's body onto the gurney and into the ambulance. Karl, his arms hanging limply along his sides, climbed into the front seat. Paul, with a smeared painted smile on his face, sat beside her in the back. Hans and Heinrich stood together and watched the vehicle move steadily toward the exit.

* * *

Three hours later, Paul, Karl and his sons Hans and Heinrich returned to the Zimmermann RV in the Big E parking lot for staff and workers. After the trip to the hospital, they had gone directly to the funeral home.

They had also met with the West Springfield city police to review the events, ruling out any other cause than accidental. The family assured the authorities that they had checked all of their equipment carefully, as they do before every performance. While the investigation was going on at the scene, the remaining performances of the entire circus for the afternoon and evening were cancelled.

* * *

Paul, disheveled and worn, still in his clown outfit and face, fell across the large bed. Anna's father went into the bathroom and closed the door. he shower was turned on. Outside, it was already early evening. A few minutes later, the shower stopped. Karl emerged, wearing work clothes but his face washed clean and stance erect. He said, "Hans, Heinrich and I have agreed that we will perform tomorrow when the investigation is complete. We need our rest tonight to prepare for tomorrow. Paul, have you changed your mind yet about coming back to the circus ring in the morning?"

Paul answered, "No. I cannot go back there. I will stay in my trailer overnight. It is too much for me to return so soon. I don't understand how you can do it."

Karl, the grieving father, turned towards Paul. "My family and I must go back up there tomorrow. It is what Anna would want us to do. She was completely confident that she was ready today. It is so hard to be sure what is best. I had asked her to wait longer, with more practice, before doing it. But you know, she wanted so much to do the double exchange."

Paul put on his coat to go outside, back to his own trailer. He said to Karl, "I still cannot understand your courage."

"Our family must go on because we love her. There is really no choice for us."

As he gently closed the door, Paul said to Karl, "Take care. And I loved her too."

Karl replied, "I know. We all loved her and Paul, she loved you very much."

* * *

In the circus arena the next morning, the circus master began the show with a period of silence to remember Anna and to pray for comfort and support to the Zimmermann family. Within moments, the show began with the traditional opening acts. The equestrian performance thrilled the audience and was almost over. Hans, Heinrich and Karl were sitting on some crates beside the side entrance into the arena. They were waiting for their cue to climb up the ladders. The horses pranced out of the ring. Karl nodded and his two sons stood up, stretched their muscles, and started towards the entrance.

From around the corner, a bright, smiling clown and donkey came toward them. Paul stopped long enough beside them to say, "The show must go on." Then, he slapped the donkey and chased it into the circus ring. The bright lights and sounds of the band, the clapping of the crowd, the shouts of the vendors offered testimony to Anna's life and courage.

A SECOND CHANCE–ELLEN'S STORY

SPRINGFIELD AND WEST SPRINGFIELD | 2011

I was nervous about going to my twenty-fifth high school reunion in May 2011 in Springfield. Actually, I was almost petrified with fear. I really did not want to go back where I had so many memories, even though most of them were positive.

My late husband Mark and I had both graduated from Classical High School in 1986. After high school, we attended Springfield College and became engaged during our sophomore year there. We were married two years later in Marsh Memorial Chapel on the campus, the day after our graduation in 1990. It was convenient to combine our college commencement day with our wedding one day later so that our family and friends could celebrate both exciting events on the same weekend.

Now, twenty-five years later, I would be returning to Classical alone, without Mark, for the Saturday reunion. My married name was Mrs. Ellen Jackson, but I was anxious because each time I would be meeting someone I would need to explain my name. Although I had been living in West Springfield for about fifteen years across the Connecticut River where I taught English courses at West Springfield High School, I would be returning to see many of our old friends. Well, we are not really so old, all of us in our mid-forties.

My twenty-year-old daughter, Tanya, had reassured me, "You really should go. Like, it would be good for you to get away for one day. Sort of a mini-vacation."

"But, sweetheart", I responded, "it will be difficult seeing people that your father and I knew together. I will have to repeat again and again the news that your father is dead. That I am a widow."

"Mom, you are a courageous person. I understand it will be difficult, but you will also be able to receive their comfort and support. You know, like you have always taught me to face my fears and be honest about how I am feeling."

It had been hard adjusting to the many new responsibilities after Mark's sudden death from a heart attack in 2009. I knew I had to go to the reunion, even if it would bring up my sadness. But I would also recall memories of happy times with Mark while we were students together. This was another step in learning how to live alone. Every day brought some new frightening experience, but after I had gone through each day, day by day, I felt more confident. Some people told me: "Time will heal" or "you will get over it". They don't understand. I don't think I will ever really get over losing him.

I had much for which to be thankful. At the time of Mark's death, my two children were helpful and they were both doing well in school. Tanya had just finished her junior year at Bay Path University and was in a steady relationship. Mark, Junior, was working full time after his graduation from college in 2007. Their active lives had helped to fill the void left by the loss of their father. Soon, both of my children would be living away from home. I dreaded the future and more loneliness, but also knew each of them would do well in their own independent lives.

Because I lived so close to the reunion venue at the downtown Sheraton, I decided to attend only Saturday and not stay at the hotel. It was a fifteen minute drive from my home on Piper Road in West Springfield to the events at the hotel and Classical Condominiums. Saturday morning I skipped the hotel breakfast and went directly to our former school building.

Our Class of 1986 was the last group to graduate from Classical High School before it closed down. Mrs. Ann Southworth was interim principal during our senior year. The new Springfield Central High School opened in 1985. Three years after our graduation the old high school had been converted into condominiums and opened for sale. Several months after we had been married, Mark and I visited during the open house for the new units in 1990. We had been impressed how the interior of the building had been beautifully preserved. The classrooms and other spaces had been remodeled into attractive units, each one varying in shape and features depending on the size and arrangement of the original classroom. Each unit had high ceilings with brick walls and high windows with views overlooking the parking lot, State Street, up the street towards Commerce High School, or to the back overlooking Temple Street, all distinctly urban views.

The main entrance on State Street opened into the large atrium with its grand staircase and high ceiling. There were parking spaces for condo owners in front of the entrance, within the basement area and in the adjacent parking lot used by the Springfield City Library and Springfield Museums on State Street.

Now in May of 2011, I was back for my twenty-fifth high school reunion. I registered at the welcome table in the atrium, put on my name tag with my yearbook photo and chatted with the welcoming host and hostess. Several of the units were open for visits by our classmates. I visited some of my favorite classrooms and met the current owners. Carol Costa, who taught English at Classical while I was a student, welcomed me into her condo. There was no **Scribe** published during our senior year. Mrs. Costa was the faculty advisor and in its place our writing class published "The Best of **Scribe**", including samples from past issues.

In the atrium, I soon reunited with Joan and David. Joan had been one of my best friends at Classical but we had lost touch after they had moved to the Chicago area. We began recalling incidents of activities together, laughing and picking up just as if we had been in touch all these years. I relaxed, realizing that I was enjoying this reunion after all.

There were a few copies of our 1986 **Blue and White** yearbook to look at. Our yearbook was dedicated to Jennifer Salisbury, one of our classmates who had died. The inscription declared: 'Each person will hold different memories of CHS. Some will remember it as the place where he or she spent the best years of his or her life, the place where everlasting friends were made, or the building blocks to success." Jennifer Salisbury 1968-1986 had written before her death "Dreams are made of people, and people are of dreams." "Life is such a wonderland where nothing's what it seems."

Our senior year was the first time a Pep Squad had been formed. Our Class Song was "Party all the time" and our Class saying "Where's the party?" The girls were especially into fashion- one popular haircut style was to grow half of one side of the hair at shoulder length and the other half side shaved or cut above the ear. Hair became a form of expression- radical, soft, curly or bobbed. Dyed hair was definitely very popular. Almost all shirts and sweaters were oversized, while pants were tight and cropped at the ankles. Madonna had an influence on some of our fads of wearing lace shirts, lace pants and tube clothing.

Informal activities included playing hacky sac by flipping a bean bag ball with one's feet. Skate board and dirt bike gymnastics were also emerging. The crushes and infatuations seemed to be the most important part of our high school experiences as we fell in and out of love. It was a central part of our high school days and growing up.

Joan, David and I walked over to the Sheraton for an informal buffet lunch. The air of May was fresh and clear, filled with the fragrance of the lilac blossoms. Daffodils and tulips were blooming in the gardens in front and in planters along the sidewalks of the condominiums. The trees were completely filled with emerging leaves. It was hard to believe that only a month ago that most of the trees were just beginning to bud. The weather was cool with mostly a clear blue sky and some small cirrus clouds on the horizon above the city.

As I came into the dining room I saw Tom Hopkins. Tall and dignified with a distinctive moustache and a lean, athletic appearance. He had not changed much at all from his varsity days as a teammate with Mark on the football and baseball teams. I went to him as our classmates were trying to recall faces and names. As memories were jarred and connections made, the conversations became more animated.

I reached out my hand, "Tom, I'm Ellen Jackson. Do you remember me?"

"Oh, yes. How could I forget you? You were usually the bounciest of all the cheerleaders. I was sorry to hear about Mark two years ago. His heart attack was so sudden."

I said, "Your flowers were beautiful. I'm sorry I never wrote much back. But Mark was the letter writer between us. How is Marjorie? Has she come with you this weekend?"

"I should have written. She died last October after she was diagnosed with pancreatic cancer that spread very quickly. I was so involved with her care, that I never notified any one. I'm sorry."

"I'm the one who should be sorry. I know that it is not easy to lose your loved one and life partner. I never knew her, except that you did bring her back here for our tenth reunion, fifteen years ago."

"Yes, she enjoyed that. But it is a relief that she died quickly. She was suffering so much. She was able to have hospice care in the hospital near our home in Ludlow even to the very last days. The chemotherapy and the radiation treatments had little effect and the side-effects were debilitating. She was tired and uncomfortable or in pain the last several months."

We reminisced about each other's spouses for a long time. It was good to talk with someone who understood how devastating the loss of a mate and lover is. I told Tom, "Most of my friends and colleagues in West Springfield have been either married or single and could not truly empathize with my feelings. Some of them withdrew from me because they could not identify with me, did not know how to help, or were busy with their own lives."

"I wish that I had known. I wondered why I didn't receive your usual delightful Christmas card."

Tom said, "I just didn't have the energy or the spirit to send Christmas greetings. I know it was selfish, but I was sad and depressed for several months after Marjorie's death. But then I realized that life must go on, and I have two wonderful sons to live for. Patrick, my youngest son is going to Holyoke Community College."

"Really, my Tanya is entering her senior year at Yale. She has loved all her time there."

Tom continued, "And George, my oldest son, is developmentally delayed, living with a couple other young men in a home in Ludlow. He works every day in a work center. He is doing well for himself and enjoys his friends and his supporters. "

Tom said, "It seems that our high school property survived our class. It looks even better now. I remember the grounds and maintenance people, and the directors of the cafeteria and dining room. Now we are the returning alumni. I am impressed. "

At the table where we sat for the light buffet lunch, two of the women had never married and were mostly interested in talking about their careers. Each of them celebrated their freedom as single persons to pursue their own interests. I found myself defending marriage, children and a career. I emphasized that it takes stamina and cooperation to combine all aspects but that it was worth the problems, to enjoy the joys.

We walked back to the Classical Condominiums and gathered again in the atrium to share more memories. Our class president, George Dipscomb, led the discussion.

During our memory sharing, I reported "I had performed in Ibsen's **Doll House** in our senior play. I played Nora. Several years later my own real-life marriage was very different from the marriage depicted in the play. I was treated like an equal. I was able to be independent and become who I was while I was married. In many of our marriages, there has been mutual respect for each other's roles."

Several classmates shared about some of their volunteer activities during our high school years: Springfield City Library, Stage West, churches, Baystate Medical Center, Boy Scouts. A few shared their adventures learning how to drive and then with their new licenses. We recalled the diversity of students while we attended high school, characterized with different names, such as preppies, jocks, brains, computer whizzes, musicians, artists, writers, actors, singers.

Our school spirit bonded all students to a common feeling of companionship in and outside of the school. Most of us were enthusiastic for school activities. Our morale often went up and down, based on sports teams, music groups and other clubs. Many activities kept us busy: **Blue and White** yearbook, the student newspaper **Recorder,** Majorettes; Jazz-Rock singers; Band, Classical Senate, Madrigal Singers, student patrol. Senior class coffee shop, school library, mathematics, African American Society, Drill team, ski club, As Schools match wits, Audio visual reps, drama club, Classical concert chorale.The major sports included softball, track (boys and girls), tennis, golf, gymnastics, football, soccer (boys and girls), cross country, basketball (boys and girls), wrestling, ice hockey, and swimming (boys and girls).

On July 13, 1985, after our junior year, some of us drove down in two cars to Philadelphia for the Live Aid- Feed the World concert, broadcast live from Wembley Stadium in London and linked by satellite to the US. We loved seeing the world-famous musicians performing to raise funds for the hungry facing the terrible famine in Africa. One of our favorite groups was Queen, playing some of their big hits like *Bohemian Rhapsody*.

One classmate said, "We will never forget when Sharon McAulliffe, the teacher from Concord, NH, and all the crew members on the space shuttle "Challenger" died in January of our senior year." Another classmate recalled the two Springfield police officers, Alain Beauregard and Michael Schavina, who were killed on duty.

Another former student read the statistics of a survey of our class reported in our year book: 87% were planning on attending college or graduate school in near future. 76% said Yes to the question Do you think there should be another space shuttle after the fate of the Challenger? 58% reported Yes to Do you agree with the anti-apartheid movement? 15% Yes, 59% No to the question: Do you think you will live to see a nuclear war take place?"

I told Tom "Mark had served in the Navy on an aircraft carrier during Operation Desert Shield off the coast of Kuwait and Iraq."

Tom replied, "I was deployed during the same time for one tour of duty in Kuwait with the Army National Guard."

The reunion committee had created several display boards for us to recall our past times. Famous Classical alumni/ae were highlighted with their class year: Congressman Edward Boland 1928, Theodor Geisel 1921, Frank Freedman, Federal judge 1943, Charles Ryan Mayor, 1944, William Manchester, author 1940, Adele Addison opera and stage star 1942.

On our tour of the building and small outdoor area, we noticed that the small oak tree was now grown much larger. While visiting around Classical, in the afternoon, tentatively, he took my hand in his. I felt twenty-five years younger. But I felt awkward, as if I still belonged to Mark. I was confused. I wasn't married any more, but I felt strange, letting another man hold my hand. I gently pulled it away and said, "I'm sorry. I'm not quite ready for anything like that." He was courting me. Or as my daughter would say, "He was coming on to me." I wanted him but I also felt that I was not ready.

With such understanding in his words, he looked at me with his brown eyes and said, softly, "I understand. I don't mean to rush you. We have both been lonely."

We used to eat at the Friendly's or McDonald's on State Street after home games. Whenever I wanted to get away from the high school cafeteria food, one of my favorite places was Friendly's, although that one was now closed. I usually ate a fish fry platter, French fries, tartar sauce, cole slaw and a Fribble milk shake.

As Tom and I walked outside along the sidewalk and the parking lot outside Classical, I heard some whistling in the shrubs. He said "Sounds like a warbler." I replied, "No, I think it's a sparrow." "No, they are hard to see, but it is definitely a warbler." Just then, we could see a flitting movement of yellow in the branches. He exclaimed "It's a yellow warbler. See the small, straight bill. He is looking for insects to eat. They migrate to the Canadian woods after spending the winter in Mexico or

Latin America. Almost pure yellow, with a few reddish brown streaks."

"I still keep the postcards that you sent Mark and me from your business trips. Where have you been travelling lately?"

He answered," I've lost all interest in travel. Much of the pleasure was in sharing with Marjorie. Now, I can't get excited about going places alone. Who can I talk about the different places with? My real estate work keeps me busy all year."

At our Saturday evening reunion banquet at the Sheraton, several of our classmates joined us at the same table, including Mary and Dave. Tom and I were able to sit together and continue our conversation. The whole class sang some of our favorite songs. The cheerleaders were rounded up to lead some cheers. Over the past twenty-five years cheerleading has become far more gymnastic and athletic.

I was aware that Tom was watching me while I was talking with Mary and Dave. I began to feel like I was on a first double date or a group date in high school. On those first high school gatherings, the larger group of friends became part chaperone and part emotional support.

All of the music played as background during dinner included hits from our high school years: "Fall of 1983"and "Baby Jean" by Bruce Springsteen. Tom commented that that song looked back at teenage years and the memories of seeking and finding friends to run with, riding in cars and listening to records. And "Dancing in the Dark" with its words "getting up in the evening coming home in the morning…this gun's for hire even if we're just dancing in the dark." Other songs from our high school time included: Elton John's "I Guess That's Why They Call it the Blues", Billy Joel's "An Innocent Man" and Cyndi Lauper's "Girls Just Want to Have Fun."

MTV was three years old in 1984 and had become the highest-rated basic cable network in America with mostly teenage and young adult viewers. Return of the Top 40 and singles still on vinyl but new compact discs were becoming popular.

Tom reminded us that in the summer and fall of 1984, our junior year, Springsteen and the E Street Band were on their Born in the USA Tour and a new female vocalist, Patty Scialfa, joined the band. "My Hometown" about his home in Freehold, New Jersey expressed his memories and the divide between the haves and the have-nots. Each stop on the tour supported local programs such as local food banks or political organizations and health clinics. The tour ended in January 1985.

In May of our Junior year the "We Are the World" record, a benefit for USA for Africa, was made at a live concert in Los Angeles, with many musicians who had been recruited by Springsteen.

In February of our senior year the E Street Band began its "Tunnel of Love Express Tour", including an April concert in Worcester. Tom and five of his friends went to Worcester; I went with three of my girlfriends. We didn't know the two groups had attended the same concert and were fans of The Boss until our current reunion.

As Saturday evening and the reunion came to a close, Tom and I knew that we had enjoyed each other's company. Tom suggested that we see each other again. Some time. "When I have a day free this summer I can come visit you. How would that be?"

"It would be difficult for me. I don't think I am ready yet for another friendship."

"How about just to be friends. Who share some common memories and mutual friends. Nothing more."

I was mixed up, drawn to want to spend some more time, not wanting the reunion day to end, but afraid of the future. I had made things so definite.

I said, "Thanks anyway but I don't think we should see each other. This was a nice reunion. But let's leave it at that."

After the banquet I drove the short trip back home. The reunion was over. When I walked in the front hall, Tanya greeted me with "Did you meet any eligible bachelors today?"

"No, honey. But I did meet a handsome widower my age."

"Well when are you going to invite him over for dinner?"

"You wouldn't mind?"

"No, of course not. You need a friend. A male friend."

All that night, I could hardly sleep, recalling all the people and activities. I dreamt that I was taking a final exam and was sitting in front of the exam questions unable to recall anything about the subject. I woke up relieved to realize that I was only dreaming.

* * *

On the next day, I looked up Tom's contact information in our reunion directory. Monday evening I called him, "Tom, this is Ellen. Could

I have a second chance at your offer to get together? When is that next vacation of yours?"

"Sure, you can have a second chance. I've got a busy week and next weekend with house showings and some closings. But, let's keep in touch."

Over the next several months we got together several times, and talked on the phone most evenings. As our relationship developed, there were several conversations about living together. We discussed selling both of our houses and finding a new neutral place, but we also wanted to keep the memories of our deceased spouses alive. I said "with my work as a high school teacher it would be harder for me to move to a different school district and my current home is close to the West Springfield High School so I prefer to remain where I am."

Tom replied "Being a real estate agent I can live anywhere. I can still associate with my brokerage office in Springfield and continue with current clients. As I learn more about the West Springfield area market, we can move into your house." Within the next few months, combining all of our belongings into one residence, we held a yard sale at my house and he had one at his house in Ludlow. He sold his house and moved in with me in West Springfield.

Our best free times together were weekday evenings and weekends. We got together with his sons, Patrick and George, and my children, Tanya and Peter, to share with them our plans and all get to know each other. I often would accompany him at his open house events on Sunday afternoons. We would attend some of my school events when possible. Much of my home time was also devoted to reading and correcting papers and tests. Each year I taught Advanced Placement English and American Literature, Modern Novels, and Creative Writing. West Springfield had been my hometown for the past twenty years. But the community was not as familiar to Mark. I enjoyed introducing him to my favorite places and people. We returned to the Ludlow area for a few activities with which he had been connected and to visit his parents and his son. We began to prepare together for our wedding and agreed on a summer July wedding, during my school vacation.

Tom and I often listened to Bruce Springsteen's music and shared our experiences as they related to the themes he wrote and sang about during his career. Mark had an extensive collection of music over almost three decades that provided with us with many hours of listening to music at home. Together we came to share our appreciation for several musicians, but The Boss was clearly our favorite from our high school years to the present. In the years before we married, we realized that we had been fans of his and that mutual knowledge brought us closer together. Our favorite songs included "Nebraska", "Tunnel of Love" and "Streets of Philadelphia". We rented films for which he had written songs, including "Dead Man Walking"," The Wrestler", "Fourth of July," "Greetings from Asbury Park" and "The Ghost of Tom Joad". During our first marriages we had gone separately to the Tour of "The Rising" concert on November 19, 2007 at Fenway Park in Boston. I had gone with some of my colleagues; Tom had gone with his wife Marjorie.

We realized we had attended several home Red Sox games over the years, but never connected with each other. This included being present when the Red Sox won the World Series October 27, 2004, for the first time since 1918. Eight months after the hurricane Katrina hurricane hit New Orleans, Springsteen had performed at New Orleans Jazz and Heritage Festival. "We Shall Overcome: the Seeger Sessions" from the album and tour.

November 19, 2007 Boston show of "Magic" tour. Both of us had supported Obama in the campaign of 2008. The album of "Bruce Springsteen and the E Street Band Live/1975-1985" came out. In the time after our high school graduation, cassette, vinyl and audio sales were all declining and the new technology of the compact disc became popular.

Springsteen had once declared in 1997 "When I started out, I wasn't so concerned with instantaneous success or the biggest hits as I was with making music, that would find its way into people's daily lives, that would become part of them. I wanted to find my audience, my blood brothers and sisters, somebody I could talk to who shared my concerns and my obsessions... It's the audience that gives my words its deepest meaning."

We valued Springsteen's writing and singing about the working men and women of our country, the poor and marginalized, immigrant workers, against the Vietnam war. Tom and I discussed our first marriages, our interests, passions and activities from childhood through to the most recent year of our new relationship and engagement.

We created many new experiences together as a couple and with our children. During the year of our engagement, we participated in many activities and events as a couple with family and friends. During my years married to Mark, because he was not interested in live music concerts, I had attended Big E concerts with female friends or teacher colleagues. Some of the headliner singers I enjoyed at the Big E were LaToya Jackson (1990), Beyonce with Destiny's Child (2000), Fergie of the Black Eyed Pea (2008)s, Blake Shelton (2011) and Reba McIntire (2011). But even musical events on the small concert stage were very good.

* * *

Throughout our year of engagement, Tom and I usually ate at home, shopping for food and then often preparing meals together. We also enjoyed eating out at favorite dining places in West Springfield and the area. Some of these were Hofbrauhaus, Charlie's Diner, Piccadilly Pub, Friendly's, Outback, Chili's, Memo's, Partners @ the Cup and Storrowton Tavern. Because of our different jobs we kept our two cars, a black 2010 Honda Civic and a blue 2009 Volkswagen Beetle, both of which we had maintained at Central Chevrolet. With so many household possessions being combined we did not need to shop for appliances, furniture or clothing. There were plenty of stores for shopping in our area, especially along Riverdale Street. We kept most of the rooms in my house the same, except we redecorated our bedroom to combine our uniquely personal tastes.

Tom and I attended a few shows at the Majestic, the West Springfield community theatre which offered excellent productions throughout the year. We attended the West Springfield Veterans' Day events in November and Memorial Day event on the town green in May 2012. The West Springfield mayor and the director of veterans affairs spoke at both of these program. We also attended the Memorial Day program at the Massachusetts State Veterans Memorial Cemetery in Agawam.

In the Fall of 2011, Tom and I visited the Big E, which was familiar to me personally as well as from reading all of my student essays over the years. There was a lot to see and enjoy. My favorites included the animal shows highlighting llamas, alpacas, sheep, pigs, steer and heifer, and dairy animals.

For several years I had begun each new school year in September assigning my AP 11th grade English students to write non-fiction essays or articles based on the people and activities at the Big E. There was free admission for all West Springfield students on West Springfield Day. Several of the students wrote about the New England State capitol buildings which featured arts and crafts, information about tourist attractions and the special foods and beverages representative of each state.

Some examples of the student essays about the Storrowton Village Museum included excerpts as follows: "Before law schools were founded, a student would learn about the legal profession for several years with an experienced individual lawyer in his private office. I was fascinated by the Eddy Law office, a one room building, filled with items from his career. He wrote with a quill feather ink pen. Only about six feathers were pulled from the goose to be used as a pen. If a finer or thinner line was preferred, the quills would be taken from a duck. For the thinnest lines, the quills would be taken from a crow. All of the legal documents were written by hand with beautiful and precise calligraphy."

Another student wrote about the one-room schoolhouse. "The volunteer portraying a school teacher told me that the teacher would rap the hand or bottom of a misbehaving student with a sapling. The students in the classroom would all observe this discipline, often included the younger and older siblings of the discipline student. Depending on the severity of the misdeed, the student would often receive a second disciplinary punishment at home by the mother. When the father came in from work, there would often be a third punishment. By the end of the day, the student clearly would have 'learned his or her lesson."

One of the students wrote about the history of the village itself: "Storrowton Village was created from 1927-1930 by Miss Storrow. She had arranged for the different buildings from several New Hampshire and Massachusetts towns to be disassembled, moved to the current site in West Springfield and reassembled to create an authentic recreation of a 19th century village of historical buildings from the 1700s and 1800s, around a traditional village Green. The buildings had all been either abandoned or scheduled for demolition and were all rescued to provide a place to learn about early American life throughout the entire year. For almost ninety years, the Storrowton Village Museum has provided education and entertainment for young and old."

As Tom and I were visiting different venues for our wedding and reception, we easily decided on this historical recreation of a New England village. Although the wedding could be held under the Gazebo on the green, we decided to use the 1834 Meetinghouse which would provide an indoor space for our guests in case the weather was rainy.

In late July of 2012, we celebrated our wedding in the meeting house. It was a beautiful cool and clear summer morning. Our reception dinner was held in a private dining room upstairs at the Storrowton Tavern. The Tavern is comprised of the 1789 Atkinson Tavern originally from Prescott, Massachusetts, and the 1822 Baptist Meeting House from Southwick, Massachusetts.

The meeting house has a simple, white interior and exterior, with clear glass windows and a belfry. Tom's son George was his best man; my daughter Tanya was my maid of honor. My son Peter escorted me down the aisle. Tom's younger son Patrick was an usher. Tanya and I wore casual summer dresses and carried beautiful wildflower bouquets. Tom and I offered our wedding vows to each other and exchanged our rings. Two of our friends from the music faculty at West Springfield played the violin and cello for the processional and the recessional music. The officiating clergy was the pastor of the Mittineague Congregational Church, United Church of Christ, in West Springfield. I had known him for many years through community events and activities. He stood below the high pulpit, standing behind a short wooden door, facing the guests. All of our wedding party stood in a straight line facing the pastor during the ceremony. In memory of our deceased spouses, Mark and Marjorie, we left two vacant spaces in the pew seats decorated with small bouquets. We were delighted that both of our sets of parents and our former parents-in-law were able to attend. Fifty of our friends and family attended as our guests.

After the ceremony, we greeted everyone as they came out of the meeting house. After photos on the green, we went into our reception dinner. With this meaningful and simple marriage ceremony, honoring both our past and our future, we began the next chapter of our lives together.

TONY GANDOLFO'S STORY

SPRINGFIELD | 2012

The Natural Gas Explosion

I was living by myself on the second floor on the east side of the six floor McIntosh Condominium building on the corner of Worthington Street and Chestnut Street in downtown Springfield. I had moved into this building twenty-two years earlier in 1990, several years after it had been converted into forty-one condominium units. The original building was constructed in 1913 for the McIntosh Shoe Company, at the time the largest inland boot and shoe jobbing house in New England. Its continued growth required larger quarters, and this structure was its third home. This building is the best example in Springfield of the Commercial style as typified by the "Chicago School" which included large window openings and lack of ornamentation.

The biggest event of my living there was Friday afternoon, November 23, 2012, the day of the natural gas explosion. The morning was overcast with gray clouds and cold temperature, normal for the day after Thanksgiving. I began the day with breakfast of Honey Nut Cheerios, two clementines, a blueberry muffin and coffee. I bundled up and walked the three blocks west to Main Street. Along with thousands of people, many of them families with young children, I enjoyed the annual Parade of the Big Balloons. The parade ended with Santa Claus and Mrs. Claus on the last float who went inside the Tower Square Mall to greet all the children and welcome shoppers to the stores inside the mall. I was pleased to see all the excited children. This event reminded me of my daughter Carla who had died at ten and would have been thirty years old this year if she had lived.

I came home and was reading when I noticed a commotion at Scores Gentlemen's Club at 453 Worthington Street and the corner of Chestnut Street, directly opposite the large windows of my condo. I watched many of the workers and clients quickly leaving the two-story building and running across the street towards the Mardi Gras and 350 Grill. Within minutes sirens blared as two Springfield fire engines arrived from the central fire station one block east of this corner. Police cruisers from the police headquarters three blocks away and Columbia Gas service trucks arrived. The fire alarm in our building began. Police entered and went from floor to floor urging residents to evacuate our building. I went over to the Mardi Gras and 350 Grill to wait with the large crowd evacuated from many of the businesses and residential buildings in the immediate area. I learned that a gas company crew member was taking readings when he had shouted for people to exit immediately.

About 5:20 p.m., a huge explosion with a deafening blast and powerful concussion flattened Scores. As a precaution against further explosions we were advised to stay inside and not to go outside to watch the aftermath as the firefighters put out the flames and kept watering the entire site through the night.

A dancer who worked at Scores told me "My employer gave me about 20 minutes notice to get out of the club. I came across the street to the Mardi Gras Champagne Room, where we were having a drink, and the building where I work blew up. I watched my livelihood go up before my eyes. My job just exploded."

Another dancer told me "I was on stage when the club's 'house mom' came up and told me everyone had to leave the building. I went upstairs to get my clothes, and I saw smoke coming out of the ladies room. Seconds later, the manager ran in and yelled, "Get out. Now!" I left the building and came across the street to wait. A few minutes later, there was the explosion. I feel lucky we got out." A third dancer told me "Scores workers had been smelling gas for awhile, and the gas company came in during the week to check, but didn't find anything. This morning the smell of gas was especially bad. I felt light-headed and went upstairs."

I stayed at the bar of the restaurant until it closed and watched the local evening news report updates. Springfield Mayor Dominic Sarno said, "Because the area had been evacuated, most of those injured were city and gas company workers at the scene to investigate the gas leak. The injured included nine firefighters, four Columbia Gas workers, two police officers, one Water Department worker and at least two civilians that we are aware of. But there were no fatalities, thank God."

The TV news reporters declared that the explosion leveled one downtown business, heavily damaged a dozen nearby buildings, including the McIntosh building, and blew out windows in dozens of others in a blast and shock wave. The explosion was felt as far as 10 miles away in South Hadley, Chicopee, East Longmeadow and Wilbraham. The Square One daycare next door to Scores was heavily damaged and due to the Thanksgiving holiday closed for the day. Friday evening, work was done to secure buildings that sustained broken glass. Acting Fire Commissioner Joseph Conant said investigators with his office will work with the city Arson and Bomb Squad and Columbia Gas to determine the cause and source of the leak and the cause of ignition. One man who lived in his apartment at the corner of Chestnut and Taylor streets, a block away, reported: "All of a sudden I hear the boom and all my windows blew out. All the smoke started to fill up the place. I thought someone set off a bomb."

None of us were allowed back in the McIntosh building that evening or the next few days. Many of the residents of the damaged buildings within the blast zone spent the next several days and nights in an emergency shelter at Central High School which was made available for many of the residents of the damaged buildings within the blast zone. I was able to stay with a friend for a couple of weeks who lived in the Classical Condominiums several blocks away.

Saturday I walked around the blocks surrounding the explosion site. Inspection teams arrived Saturday morning to assess the damage to buildings in the area of the blast zone. The Scores building was totally demolished, and I could see as many as twelve buildings in the immediate vicinity which sustained serious structural damage. Another dozen or more sustained broken windows. Much of the damage was to the high-rise buildings in the area of Worthington and Chestnut Streets. Firefighters on aerial platforms were removing broken glass from the upper floors of the buildings in the vicinity. There was a lot of debris hanging off many buildings. The blast zone included much of the downtown Entertainment District. In the aftermath, the district was depopulated and its many bars, clubs and restaurants closed. For blocks in every direction, shards of glass from plate glass windows blown out by the shock wave littered sidewalks. Work was being done on Saturday and Sunday to secure buildings that had broken windows.

Saturday at a televised press conference, Mayor Sarno announced that the city was still trying to gauge the amount of damage and the economic impact to downtown businesses that will be forced to close or even relocate. "We are trying to wrap our arms around this as we move forward." Lt. Gov. Timothy Murray, said "this was a miracle on Worthington Street that no one was killed." City Building Inspector Steven Desilets said the two story building, is now "a hole in the ground." State Fire Marshal Stephen Coan credited the decision by city fire and police with the low death and injury numbers: "They took the call for what could have been a routine call of odor of gas and they took precautions. I want to wish a speedy recovery to all the first-responders who were injured in the blast, as well as the citizens who were hurt."

Columbia Gas Spokeswoman Sheila Doiron reported Saturday that company officials would be working with city and state officials to find answers. She said the company had no record dating back to 2001 to indicate any prior complaints in that area of the city. Following the explosion, gas crews with detection equipment searched several blocks in all directions but found no traces of natural gas.

I was deeply grateful that the emergency first responders, firefighters, police and emergency medical personnel had all arrived quickly and helped prevent a greater catastrophe and cared efficiently and quickly for the injured. I have a personal habit that whenever I hear the sirens of police, fire or ambulances I pause and offer a prayer for the safety of all the first responders and all those involved in the emergency as victims or survivors. This time I was praying even more as I was fully aware of what was happening in my neighborhood.

My Passion for Family and Faith

Let us go back to the earlier time of my life as I share with you my life story. I was born at Mercy Hospital in 1952, and with my parents and two older sisters, I lived in the South End of Springfield. I was baptized and had my first Communion at Our Lady of Mount Carmel Parish one block west of South Main Street. This parish was established in 1907 and was in the predominantly Italian neighborhood. Most of the families were second and third generation immigrants from Italy. With the displacement of many homes and businesses in the 1960's, during the construction of I-91, our family moved to the Hungry Hill section of the city. While we were living in our new home we went to the parish school of Our Lady of Hope parish at the corner of Carew Street and Armory Street. My father had died of lung cancer when I was sixteen and my mother from pneumonia when I was eighteen. After their deaths, my two older sisters took care of me and raised me for several years in the same house.

In 1972, two years after graduating from Cathedral High School on Surrey Road, I married Maria in the large sanctuary at Our Lady of Hope. We had started dating while we were both in high school. She was a beautiful bride wearing a fancy silk brocade gown with a long train. Her long black hair was wrapped around her head in curling ringlets. I wore a black suit which highlighted my own raven black curly hair which I regularly kept at about three inches long. Each of us were 5 feet 6 inches tall so we also appeared to be a matching set. We had a small bridal party of six, including the two of us, and had invited forty guests.

Following our marriage, Maria and I moved into the house where she had grown up to share living quarters and expenses with her parents. It was a large twelve room Stick style house on Ingersoll Grove in the Hill-McKnight neighborhood. This residential style was derived from the Gothic Revival style and included: a gable roof with trusses at the gable ends, horizontal, vertical and diagonal bands on the exterior wall surface, and wood clapboards, sometimes in combination with shingles. The first floor, with its kitchen, pantry, dining room and living room, was shared by all of us. Maria's parents lived on the second floor with a bathroom shared by all of us. Maria and I lived on the third floor with its dormer rooms and windows. This gave each of us privacy but the ability to visit with each other every day and share our lives as we wished. At the start, the four of us shared the use of one automobile and ate most of our meals together. In the following years, both of my sisters married Italian men and moved from Hungry Hill to separate homes in Agawam. Soon their families had expanded with two children each.

Our daughter Carla was born on the Feast of the Assumption, August 15, 1974, at St. Mercy Hospital. She was baptized at Our Lady of Hope church and attended the elementary and middle parish school next door to the church. Maria's mother, my mother-in-law, was very helpful with helping to raise Carla and they shared mutually in taking care of the house. Both my father-in-law and I were working every day during the week. We regularly attended mass at Our Lady of Hope, which was founded in 1907 and moved into a stone building in 1926. We often would also attend activities at Mount Carmel in the South end which sponsored many events to celebrate the Italian history and culture.

Once Carla was old enough to attend full-day kindergarten, Maria began two years of study at Springfield Technical Community College (STCC), located several blocks away on State Street, to prepare for employment as a medical technician.

One of our weekly family activities with all three generations was to eat together on Sunday afternoon after we had attended mass. Usually we ate at home, but we also often alternated one Sunday eating at an Italian restaurant and the next Sunday eating at a Chinese buffet. Carla was very particular about which foods she preferred, often selecting mostly lightly cooked vegetables and fresh fruit, vegetables and salads. As Carla grew older she clearly preferred healthy foods, a habit that she learned from both my wife and myself. Of course, with her mother and grandmother doing much of the cooking at home she learned to appreciate home-cooked Italian recipes. She also learned how to help in the kitchen; set table, cut up salad, other forms of food preparation and clean up after meals. We enjoyed cooking pasta of all types, spaghetti and meat balls, eggplant parmigiana, lasagna, ravioli and more.

Carla helped Maria and me decorate the exterior of the house, the front yard and a small tree during the various holidays and seasons: winter snowflakes and snowmen, red hearts for Valentine's Day, spring and Easter flowers and bunnies, Halloween creatures in October. We sometimes would also decorate the trim of the front porch with red, white and blue bunting from Memorial Day through the Fourth of July and with strings of Christmas lights in December. We also decorated some of the rooms on the first floor for these holiday periods.

Soon after Carla's birth we became family members of the Springfield Quadrangle of Library and Museums. This was one of our favorite frequent local places to go since the permanent and temporary exhibits, family events and programs always provided new entertainment and learning. Maria and I agreed that the Quadrangle is "one of the finest hidden treasures of western Massachusetts".

We were annual members of Forest Park and went there regularly throughout Carla's childhood, enjoying every facet of the park depending on the season. These included the Zoo, tennis courts, softball and baseball diamonds, soccer field, bocce court, swimming pool, ice skating rink, basketball court, walking trails and picnic areas. There were also other city parks throughout Springfield that we frequented for outdoor walking, biking, picnics and recreation. As Carla went from tricycle to bicycle, Maria and I also bought our own adult bikes to enjoy family rides together.

Carla's bedroom began as her nursery and was changed as she grew older with more appropriate decorations and furniture. She kept most of her stuffed animals, toys and dolls from her early childhood. Her favorite color white remained constant as the curtains, bedspread, rugs and wall decorations changed. The play area transformed into a study area with desk and chair, the dresser and table with a mirror also reflected her growth and different wardrobe. The hangings and posters on the walls and the books on her bookshelves reflected her developing personal interests.

Carla flourished in the parish schools and enjoyed all of her subjects, teachers and her classmates. Most of her catechism classes were part of her school curriculum. She remained friends with several of her classmates through the years and often spent free time with some of them at each other's homes. She took part in the school chorus and music groups and played the available girls' sports in each season.

Carla had a pet cat, Snowball, all white with a gray spot on the top of her head. Carla cared for Snowball, feeding her daily and changing the litter box. Snowball was an inside cat and Carla loved to pet and cuddle her cat and let her sleep on her bed every night.

On several of Carla's birthdays the three of us went to New York City on my day off. On August 15,1980 we went to see the Broadway production of **Annie**. We all enjoyed the story of Annie and her friends in the orphanage as they struggled to live under the oppression of Miss Hannigan. The ending of hope in the midst of the Great Depression was a positive story of children and love. For weeks after, at home Carla would often sing "It's the Hard Knock Life" and "Tomorrow". When the film version came out, we went to see it in 1982 and Carla was singing the songs again. The refrain of "The sun will come out tomorrow!" reflected her own positive personality. On this trip we also rode on the double-decker upper Manhattan tour bus and visited the Museum of Natural History, Central Park and St. Patrick's Cathedral.

On August 15, 1984, we went to see **Cats** which had opened on Broadway the year before and won seven Tony Awards. Different from most musicals which were based on a plot and a story, **Cats** was based on a collection of poems by T.S. Eliot and set to music by Andre Lloyd Webber. I loved it for its spectacular setting in a garbage dump. The unique personality of each feline character was brought alive by the costume and makeup. My most beloved songs were "Memory" sung by Grizabella and "Mr. Mistoffelees" sung by Mistoffelees and Rum Tum Tigger. The choreography and music were delightful and fantastic. I especially enjoyed "The Jellicle Ball" and "The Journey to the Heavyside Layer" sung and danced by the company.

Due to my work schedule It was always enjoyable when I could devote my time off to spend with my beloved family. Aside from our times together at home or in the Springfield area, these day trips were memorable. Our times together were filled with love and joy, laughter among the three of us. Maria was always an affectionate and caring wife and mother.

Carla's Farewell

Carla was healthy all of her childhood, with occasional colds, sinus and ear infections. In October of 1984, when she was ten, she developed a cold. We kept her home from school for a couple of days. Then the cold turned into flu-like symptoms with headache, fever and chills and overall weakness and lack of energy. After another two days of the flu symptoms, we drove her to the ER of Mercy Hospital on Stafford Street. After several hours in the ER the doctor decided to admit her for more observation.

The hospitalist, or hospital medical doctor, met upstairs with Maria and me. She told us "Carla has symptoms of pneumonia. These include a cough producing mucus that is gray or yellow, chest pain, rapid or difficult breathing, fever and chills. There are two kinds of pneumonia-one caused by a virus and the other by bacteria. We will take a bacterial culture to determine which kind she has." After many hours of waiting for the results, the hospitalist met with us again and reported "Carla has pneumococcal disease."

I asked, "what is that?"

The doctor explained "It is a big name for illness caused by a tiny bacterium, *Streptococcus pneumoniae*. These illnesses can be mild, such as ear and sinus infections. But they can also be very serious. The two most dangerous pneumococcal diseases are pneumonia and meningitis. Pneumonia is an infection that inflames the lungs, filling them with liquid and making it hard to breathe. This is what Carla has."

"What is the other kind of pneumococcal disease?"

"Meningitis. This is an infection that inflames the membranes around the brain and spinal cord. Both are extremely dangerous and can lead to sepsis. Sepsis is a life-threatening response to infection in our body. To take precautions, we are moving your daughter into the ICU to a restricted room where she can be treated. Everything that we do will be to support her and provide her with the best treatment." After she was moved to her new isolated room we went in to see her. We had to put on a sanitary face mask and a sanitary gown to protect ourselves and prevent bringing in any other risks to her. She was receiving oxygen to help her breathing, an IV to provide medication and hydration and hooked to a heart monitor. The sign on her door required staff and visitors to wear a mask and gown. Visitors were restricted to immediate family for short periods of time.

Within the next day, the doctor informed us that Carla's body was becoming septic, the life threatening response to the infection. Due to her weakened immune system from her cold, the streptococcus pneumonia spread quickly. Over the next two days the sepsis caused confusion, disorientation, shortness of breath, fever and chills, a high heart rate, extreme pain, and sweaty skin. The doctor told us, "we often don't know when someone has sepsis except that the patient feels very, very sick and is very, very weak. Sepsis is usually diagnosed in a hospital via tests for infection. The vital organs become damaged. You need to be prepared for the worst. She could die from the infection soon."

The Catholic hospital chaplain came and offered prayers and the sacraments for Carla and for us. He tried to comfort us as we prepared for her imminent death.

After losing consciousness and slipping into a coma, Carla died within the next day, November 2nd. Maria and I were in shock even though we had been staying in the hospital day and night. We had continued to hope that she would improve and recover. The doctors and nurses told us that everything that they could have done was done. They shared their support and empathy for us. We were heart broken. Much of the next few days was a total blur. Carla, our one and only child, our beloved daughter, was dead at the age of ten. The only positive sign we had was that she died on All Soul's Day and we shared the faith and assurance that she had entered eternal life with God on the very holy day to remember all those who have died.

As we tried to make arrangements, for her funeral and burial, I wanted to know how common this disease was. I was able to learn on the internet that the leading causes of death, for children ages 10-14, ranked from most common to least common were: unintentional injury, suicide, malignant neoplasms, congenital anomalies, homicide, heart disease, chronic low respiratory disease, cerebrovascular, influenza and pneumonia, and benign neoplasms. I had never imagined that there were so many causes of death for young children and that our daughter would succumb to one of them.

After a wake at Forastiere Family Funeral Home in the south end, the funeral mass was held at Our Lady of Hope. During the wake and in the time before the funeral mass, many people from her life and ours came and shared their condolences and support with us. All of her classmates and their parents and teachers attended both the wake and the mass. The dominant color of the array of roses and carnations were her favorite color: white.

During the mass at Our Lady of Hope, my thoughts were only of her and her short life. I did not even look at the stained glass windows that often were so inspirational and uplifting to me. I was inconsolable. My wife and I held each other tightly and we both were sobbing much of the mass. Carla's remains were buried at St. Michael Cemetery on State Street.

My wife and I grieved in our own ways. Over the next several months, we drew apart during our bereavement. After a few weeks I returned to driving and poured my emotions into working hard and focusing on the trips. Maria remained home from work for several months, sharing with her parents, but with my becoming less present. Carla had been the center of our lives, and we both were terribly sad, but we grieved separately, and regretfully not in support of each other.

Two years before Carla's death, I had revealed to Maria my bisexual preference. I had kept faithful to our marriage vows and I had not had any relations with another man or woman. We had agreed to keep my orientation secret from Carla. We had continued to be intimate and sleep in the same bed. However, after her death Carla and I agreed to seek a dissolution of our marriage with the Church. At this time, I came out as bisexual with my friends and family. For many years, I had known privately my orientation but stayed together for the marriage and for Carla. I moved out of our home. After attending the diocesan marriage tribunal and completing all the required documents, our marriage was annulled in 1987.

My Passion for Work

In the first several years of our marriage I worked in some temporary jobs, often as a livery driver using our personal car. After getting a commercial drivers license in 1976, at the age of twenty-four, I started as a full time bus driver for Peter Pan Bus Lines. The company was owned by the Picknelly family. The ancestors of their family lived in the village of Picariello, in the inland province of Avellino, thirty miles northeast from Naples. My paternal ancestors had come from Gaeta, a coastal town south of Naples. Both families had immigrated to the United States from southern Italy and settled in Springfield. The founder of the bus company had also been a livery driver in New Jersey before he started the bus company.

I learned that Peter C. Picknelly founded Peter Pan Bus Lines as a private, family-owned company in 1933. He considered the bus drivers a very important part of his family company. He recognized the drivers as the central link between management and the customers or passengers. Especially with the drivers, he stressed courtesy, helpfulness and safety as their primary concerns. The performance of drivers was closely monitored and documented. A program had been established to recognize and reward its best drivers. In 1962, Peter C. Picknelly reorganized his company with a new department for motorcoach charter trips, and a new corporation separate from Peter Pan Bus Lines, for the motorcoach tours, named Peter Pan World Travel. Peter Pan Bus Lines continued to handle regular intercity transportation and their vehicles were also called motorcoaches due to the enhancements of the interior.

When Peter C. Picknelly died suddenly in 1964, the entire company was left to his widow, Jennie, and his son Peter L. Picknelly, who was named president at the age of thirty-three. In 1974, the company converted the entire fleet of their motorcoaches to those manufactured by Motor Coach Industries. During the 1967 Montreal EXPO Peter Pan World Travel provided a daily schedule of tours to Montreal, including booking overnight stays for all passengers. In 1969, Peter L. Picknelly built a new Springfield Bus Terminal which opened at 1776 Main Street and Liberty Street, which also provided space for several other bus companies. In 1971 a new maintenance garage for all the motorcoaches was opened on the lot adjoining the terminal. These improvements and the consolidation of the business operations at the edge of downtown Springfield led to expansion and hiring of more staff and drivers.

A typical day as a Peter Pan driver to New York City included the following routine. I inspected my coach at the maintenance garage and drove the half-block over to the terminal bay. I collected tickets at the open door as each passenger boarded. I placed all the luggage in the underneath storage. Once inside, I verified that all the passengers were on the correct coach for their destination. At departure time I checked with the dispatcher by phone and left the terminal. If I left Springfield at 7:15 am, I then arrived at the Hartford railroad and bus terminal at 8 am. I waited fifteen minutes to load more passengers and luggage and then departed to New Britain to board more passengers. The next stop was New Haven at 9:15 am. The drive to Port Authority bus terminal in Manhattan took two hours, arriving to offload all the passengers at 11:30 am. Then, I waited for the departure time to return to Springfield via the reverse route.

When I began as a driver in 1976, it was at a positive time of the company's steady progress and successful growth. For the first ten years of my career I drove mostly charter groups to various events such as sporting events, race and dog track events, bingo and beano nights throughout New England. These charter trips served Golden Age, senior citizen, school, youth and veterans groups. During my career as a driver, I drove the different types of coaches as they were added to the fleet.

Beginning in the early 1980's I drove motorcoach tours that included the range of one-day tours to ten-day tours to destinations all over the nation and Canada. Several Destination coaches were named with large banner titles on the sides indicating where the tours were going. The 350th anniversary of the City of Springfield in 1984 was celebrated with the coach named Crossroads of New England, highlighting features of the western Massachusetts area. Other Destination or theme coaches had large exterior signs such as Downeast Maine, Washington, D.C., states of New York and Florida, the South, Pennsylvania Dutch country and Canadian destinations. I drove all of these destination tour routes during my career.

The tour drivers and tour escorts were especially trained to serve and communicate well with the passengers. Tour drivers would often tell stories or jokes, would sing, help with the luggage, and were always friendly. We would clean our buses and do extra things as needed for individual passengers. This was a major part of what I enjoyed about being a Peter Pan tour driver. The first regular scheduled bus line trips from Springfield and Hartford to New York City began in 1986 with twelve round trips a day.

The 5 Star Service symbol first appeared in 1986 on Peter Pan's first 102-inch-wide coaches. The stars represent five standards for customer service: safety, quality, dependability, satisfaction and fairness. The slogan on the side of each coach "People Professionals" was introduced in 1987. New wrap around designs were added to provide more graphic features to the exterior of each coach. In 1987 all coaches were equipped with a two-way radio communication system which connected every driver with the Springfield headquarters and with other Peter Pan drivers to alert them to weather conditions, construction or traffic delays, accidents and changes in connecting schedules.

Carmen Picknelly was vice-president of maintenance from 1970 until his retirement in 1992. He and the mechanics were integral to the safety of our driving. Each coach was checked and maintained before and after every trip. After each trip I reported any possible maintenance issues to the mechanics in the garage. I respected the excellent work of each of the mechanics and cleaners throughout my career. Carmen was succeeded by his son Tom Picknelly who became head of maintenance in 1992 and had been trained by his father since childhood. Tom was later promoted to Senior Vice President and supervised Peter Pan garages in southern New England, Maryland, Pennsylvania and the Metro NY areas. Tom's son Joe Picknelly is now the Fleet Manager for Peter Pan.

In 2004 Peter L. Picknelly died and the leadership was passed to his son, Peter A. Picknelly, the third generation of leaders of the Peter Pan enterprise. The Springfield Bus Terminal was proudly renamed The Peter L. Picknelly Transportation Center.

I continued to drive for Peter Pan full time and drove mostly for scheduled daily line routes to various cities in Massachusetts, Connecticut or the Northeast corridor. I did not drink alcohol or use drugs due to the important policy of random drug testing for drivers, but also because I always took seriously my responsibility for the safety of my passengers. Throughout my entire career I was able to maintain a top safety record. I achieved driving Three Million Miles without an accident. To put this in perspective, one million miles equals at least 12 years of accident-free driving. In total for the entire company, Peter Pan coaches travel over one million miles every year, or the equivalent of nearly 100 trips to the moon annually.

Living Alone

After the annulment of our marriage in 1987, I moved out of our home and rented an apartment in Kimball Towers on Chestnut Street for a few years. I went to local gay bars and clubs to socialize but I realized within three years that I did not have any interest in starting a relationship with another man or woman. I decided to remain single and celibate and learned to be completely independent.

In 1990, I moved into a small four-room unit on the second floor of the McIntosh Condominium building on the corner of Worthington and Chestnut Streets, two blocks from where I had been living the past few years. In remembrance of Carla, I placed a single electric candle, which was lit all the time, on the shelf below my living room window. This is the same room where I said my daily morning and evening prayers. I attended mass several times a week at St. Francis Chapel on Bridge Street, two blocks from my home. The Franciscan friars who lived and worked there at that time were a wonderful consolation to me.

I also loved most forms of classical music, especially opera. My favorite male opera singers were Enrico Caruso and Luciano Pavarotti. My favorite opera composers and their works came from the Romantic Age and included the following: Gioachino Rossini and his **William Tell** and

Il Barbieri di Siviglia (The Barber of Seville). Gaetano Donizetti's **Lucia di Lammermoor and Don Pasquale.** Vincenzo Bellini's **Bianca e Gernando, La Sonnambula** and **Norma.** Giuseppi Verdi's **Rigoletto, I Trovatore (The Troubador), La Treviata (The Fallen Woman), Aida, Otello and Falstaff.** Giacomo Puccini's **La Boheme, Manon Lescaut, Tosca, Madame Butterfly, La Rondine** (**The Swallow**) and **Turandot**. Except for the operas of Verdi, I believe that after the 1848 Revolution in Italy, the Italian people were never again as engrossed in opera.

After our divorce, I saw "La Cage aux Folles" on Broadway at the Palace Theatre in New York. The opening song "I am What I am" was a freeing experience for me to be out and who I am after years of living with a hidden identity. The English translation of the title is "The Cage of Crazy Women". The plot of the relationship between the protagonists George and Albin, enabling Albin to transform and come to terms with himself. The play was a coming out for gay men on Broadway who long had lived in the shadows of their clandestine home. The musical was based on a 1973 play by Jean Poiret. I had enjoyed two of Jerry Herman's Broadway musicals "Hello Dolly!" and "Mame".

I saw "Les Miserables" several times at the Broadway Theatre starting in 1987. It has become one of my favorite shows of all time. I had studied Victor Hugo's novel of the same title in high school French class and loved its adaptation to the stage in London and New York. Everything about the story and the production were amazing. Some of my favorite songs are "I dreamed a dream", "Red and Black", "A Heart Full of Love", "Do you hear the people sing?" and "Bring Him Home." The struggle and deaths of all the fighters at the barricades, including Cosete, always brought to mind the death of my beloved Carla.

I continued to attend Broadway musicals through the next thirty years whenever possible with my driving and work schedule All of them were special, but especially I enjoyed "The Phantom of the Opera", "Miss Saigon", "Crazy for You", Sunset Boulevard", "Rent", "The Lion King", "Mamma Mia!", "Moulin Rouge", "Wicked", "Billy Elliot", "Matilda the Musical" and "Shrek the Musical". Because of Carla's love of music many of these continued to remind me of her life, making me sad but also giving me new hope and purpose in my own life.

Especially I know she would have enjoyed "The Lion King" and "Matilda the Musical." Roald Dahl first published **Matilda** in 1988. It was a children's story about a brilliant little girl living with uncaring parents, who was sent away to a private school with a teacher who cared about her and a headmistress who was abusive to children. Although Carla had died four years before the book was published I read it. I enjoyed reading some children's books to nurture the child within me. After "Matilda the Musical" opened at the Shubert Theatre in New York I saw it in early 2014. 1t was a story that empowers children and reveals their importance in society.

Following our annulment, I sometimes joined my former wife and her parents on Sunday afternoons as had been our tradition during our marriage when Carla was alive. It helped that we still cared about each other and had many experiences and shared memories over the years. Especially we would gather for family birthdays. We regularly got together to celebrate the anniversary of Carla's birthday on August 15. Over the years we shared many of our memories of how she was such a wonderful daughter and grand-daughter.

Carla had usually enjoyed the variety and choices at the buffet restaurants where she could eat her favorites. She particularly liked won ton soup, egg drop soup, grilled chicken or beef mixed with broccoli and cauliflower, stir fried or sautéed food. I preferred choosing the healthier options and usually avoided fried foods. Each of us had our favorite desserts at the buffets, choosing among flan, bananas, Jello, cookies, cake, tapioca pudding, chocolate pudding and ice cream.

Some of our favorite restaurants included Theodore's, The Fort-Student Prince, Red Rose Pizzeria, Fiorentina's and Mom and Rico's. We also ate at Greek restaurants and Mediterranean restaurants such as Olympic Restaurant Deli on Chestnut Street near Congress St, operated mostly by Hispanics and mixed international menu.

In the summers I shopped at the Friday Farmer's Market. I usually walked around once to identify produce I may want; then I walked around a second time creating my menu for the week's groceries. During the year I also stopped at the Fresh from Stony Creek Farm and other restaurants in the Tower Square Food Court.

I tend to be old-fashioned. It bothered me that a waitress or store clerk greets some women without any men present "Welcome. What would you guys like?". Also, it bothers me when a waitress who doesn't know me at all, calls me "honey" or "sweetheart". If I called a woman I didn't know "honey" it would be considered sexual harassment or inappropriate.

After our divorce, I regularly ate alone at home but also ate out during my bus driving work and travel routine. This often meant still eating at one of the buffets in Springfield or West Springfield. I also enjoyed eating at one of the Italian restaurants in the city. I also liked to thank the cooks and the servers at these restaurants, many of whom I had come to know regularly, others who were new employees. One time all of the kitchen cooks and staff were eating together in the private dining area just after they had prepared and put out the dinner selections. I told them as a group: "You all do a great job. The food you prepare is always tasty, nutritious. We usually do not see you because you are busy behind the scenes in the kitchen. Thank you very much." They smiled and thanked me for recognizing their work.

I also continued to attend mass once a week at St. Michael's Cathedral, about five blocks south from my home. Although many parishioners regularly sat in the same pew every week, I preferred to sit in different sections of the sanctuary. One reason was that I liked to visit with different parishioners and get to know them. I also enjoyed looking up at the stained glass windows around the entire sanctuary and recall the meaning of each window. Because this is the cathedral and the seat of the bishop in the diocese most of the windows depicted the roles of the bishop.

For example, when I looked at the windows in the west transept, or the left side facing the altar, they illustrated the transmission the sacrament of Holy Orders from Jesus Christ to the apostles, and to the subsequent priests. These included the imposition of hands by the bishop conferring on the deacons their new status as priests with the power to teach, rule and sanctify in the Church. The scene depicted the bestowing of the instruments of the chalice containing wine and water and the paten on which the unconsecrated bread rests. Thus, this window recounted the story of a priest's ordination.

On the right or west side of the sanctuary, the transept windows depicted the Christ ascending into heaven. Christ commissioned his apostles to teach, to rule and to sanctify. Along the sides of the sanctuary are windows which revealed the different responsibilities of the bishop: the pastoral office, care of the sick, consecration of oils, dedication of churches, education and social work.

Although harder to see from the floor level, I could look backwards up above the choir balcony. Here there were two stained glass panels. These were dedicated to the two popes who have influenced liturgical art in the Church: Pope St. Gregory I and Pope St. Pius X. Other windows around the sanctuary depicted the coat of arms of four former bishops of the Diocese of Springfield and the coat of arms of the diocese itself. Others depicted St. Patrick, the apostle of Ireland, and St. Michael, the Archangel, protector of the universal church. I enjoyed studying the details of each window and learned much about the history of the church. I was reminded that in the medieval period in Europe, when most of the lay people were unable to read or write, stained glass windows in cathedrals were teaching tools. Especially when I visited the church when there was no service in progress I could sit silently, inspired by all of these windows.

Throughout my life, I knew several bishops of the Diocese of Springfield, who served the Catholics in the four counties of western Massachusetts. These were Most Rev. Christopher J. Weldon, Most Rev. Joseph E. Maguire, Most Rev. John A. Marshall, Most Rev. Thomas L. Dupre, Most Rev. Timothy McDonnell, and Most Rev. Mitchell T. Rozanski.

Then in 1990 I bought a condo unit in the newly restored McIntosh Building, in downtown Springfield. Again, I placed the electric candle in the window and kept it lit all the time in memory of Carla. I wanted to be within walking distance of my work at the Peter Pan Terminal, the Amtrak station and several PVTA bus routes. I also wanted to be close to St. Michael's Cathedral. I gave our car to Maria and decided not to buy a replacement vehicle for myself. I continued to walk a lot, travelled by the bus and eventually bought a ten-speed bicycle.

For the following twenty-two years from 1990 to 2012, I continued working for Peter Pan, visiting some of my family each week, going to mass and other community events. Eventually I stopped seeking a romantic relationship and made a conscious decision to remain celibate. As a lay person I took my own vow of celibacy and sought to deepen my daily religious life. I remained friends with several men and women but kept my relationships platonic only, or as one colleague described it: "being a friend, without benefits".

My 2008 tour to southern Italy

My grandparents had immigrated to Springfield, from Gaeta, south of Naples. In 1990 I had travelled by myself to Naples to meet and stay with several of my cousins still living in that region. Then in the spring of 2008, I took a tour with a group from St. Michael's Cathedral to the same region of southern Italy. On this second trip, I also visited with some of my cousins who were able to join our tour group at the hotel in Formia as guests during two of our dinners.

Let me share with you the highlights of this wonderful tour. On Saturday, we took a Peter Pan motorcoach to JFK Airport to fly to Rome's Fiumicino Airport, Leonardo da Vinci Airport. After our arrival, we travelled by an Italian charter bus from Rome to Grand Hotel Fagiano in Formia, on the Appian Way, our base for six nights. On the first evening, we had a bountiful welcome with a Neapolitan feast of local dishes and wine.

On Sunday, we had a full day to explore Montecassino in the morning with the group and Riviera Ulysses in the afternoon on our own. Montecassino Abbey was founded by St. Benedict about 529, becoming famous for the life and sepulcher of its founder, and as a place of holiness, culture and art. In 1944, during World War II, Montecassino was on the firing line between the Allied and Axis armies. In only three hours the entire abbey was reduced to a heap of debris where many refugees in hiding died. By the time of our visit, the abbey had been completely rebuilt and restored to its original appearance.

On Monday we went to Pompeii and Naples for the entire day. The city of Pompeii, in the shadow of the still active but dormant volcano Mount Vesuvius, is one of the archaeological wonders of the world. Pompeii was built in 7 B.C. and lasted until 79 A.D. when it was overcome by the sudden eruption of Mount Vesuvius. The city disappeared from any maps for 1,700 years and was rediscovered in the 18th century. I was most impressed in Pompeii by the reconstruction of many of the private and public buildings uncovered by archaeologists and preserved by the deep covering of pumice stone and ash since 79 A.D. Ancient Pompeii was a thriving commercial city filled with shops, markets and comfortable town houses, with paved streets, a stadium, two theatres, temples, baths and brothels. The years of excavations have revealed an intimate picture of life in the first-century Roman city.

The typical Pompeian house was built around a central courtyard or atrium whose roof sloped inwards on all four sides to a rectangular opening in the center known as the *compluvium*. Rainwater fell into a corresponding rectangular tank called the *impluviam*. Around the atrium itself were various family quarters, including bedrooms, dining rooms, vestibule and living room. Shops were built into the front of the house and sections of the house were blocked off and rented out, with separate entranceways to strangers. Many of the houses added a second story, until the Etruscan farmhouse prototype had evolved into the comfortable and palatial town houses, typified by the *Casa dei Vettii* and the *Casa del Fauno.*

After this visit, as we rode along the coastline, Mount Vesuvius loomed as the dominant feature. Our tour guide told us, "a constant plume of smoke had billowed from the cone inside the crater until 1944, when, during the volcano's last major eruption, the cone was destroyed. Today one million people reside on all sides of the volcano and below. There are thousands of early warning seismic sensors that are located all around the volcano. The people live today knowing they will be warned in advance and will have some time to evacuate the area." We then had free time to walk around Naples and enjoy the view of the Bay of Naples.

I learned about the origin of tomatoes being used as toppings on pizza. The arrival and acceptance of tomatoes in Italy marked the beginning of modern pizza as we know it. Tomatoes came from the Americas to Naples in the 17th century or earlier. Popular opinion was that tomatoes were poisonous. But the city's peasants were hungry enough that they disregarded this belief and added tomatoes on pizza. Traditional Neapolitan pizza comes in two forms: the *marinara* and the *margherita*. The *marinara* owes its name to its popularity with fishermen and sailors; it is topped with tomato, oregano, garlic, extra-virgin olive oil and fresh basil. The *margherita* is topped with tomato, basil and mozzarella.

On Tuesday, we toured Sperlonga, an ancient and picturesque old town with narrow and terraced streets. Originally it was a fortress protecting its residents from attack and invasions from many armies over the years. The local houses are built into a massive rock on a spur of land jutting out into the Tyrrhenian Sea. We visited the National Museum and the site of another villa of the Emperor Tiberius.

For lunch we stopped at a mozzarrella cheese factory, *Caseificio Casabianca*, for a tasting. That afternoon we had a guided tour of the town of Gaeta, visiting the baroque church of *Santissima Annunziata* built around 1320, the Cathedral of *St. Erasmo* with its Romanesque style from 1180, and the Sanctuary of *Montagna Spaccata*. Legend states that the "Split Mountain" divided three ways after the death of Jesus. We finished that day with dinner back at the Grand Hotel Fagiano.

On Wednesday morning we departed for a full-day on the Isle of Capri. We left from Naples Pier by Jet Napoli-Capri, a hydrofoil ferry boat which skipped above the water at a steady speed, bouncing up and down over the choppy waves. At Marina Grande, Capri, we toured by a minibus and funicular, with some shopping and sightseeing including the Piassetta. My favorite sites on Capri were the Blue Grotto and the remains of the Emperor Tiberius's villa where he retired in 27 A.D.

On Thursday, we had a full-day excursion to Sorrento and the Amalfi Coast, along one of the most beautiful drives in Europe. The peninsula included the wild and rocky coastline, caves and sea shore grottos facing the Mediterranean. We visited Sorrento, Positano and Amalfi, splendid towns in incomparable settings. I was most impressed in this area of the bountiful number of lemon groves, loaded with lemons ready for harvest. That evening we had an authentic Southern Italian farewell dinner at the hotel.

On Friday, we returned to Rome for our flight back to New York from the Leonardo Da Vinci Airport. It was a tour with many wonderful memories learning about my Italian background and strengthened our new friendships among our St. Michael's group.

Life after the gas explosion

For the next two years after the gas explosion on November 23, 2012, I relocated to Kimball Towers, one block away, while the entire McIntosh Building was renovated and approvals were given for residents to move back in. Several of my neighbors also stayed in the Kimball Towers or LaQuinta hotel. Finally, in the fall of 2014, I was able to move back into my former unit on the second floor, with brand new carpets, windows and cabinets. Some of the owners did not return after the renovations were completed and they relocated to other buildings.

Now back in my home, when I looked out from my windows, most of the buildings visible from my condo have been boarded up. I could see many vacant lots where buildings had been before. The natural gas explosion destroyed many of the adjoining buildings and left many others to be razed, awaiting future development. On the left side of Worthington St, Tyre Track tire sales and auto mechanic shop, reopened for business. On Spring Street, I could see the central Springfield Engine

1 fire station. Beyond my view there were several businesses and apartment buildings. Pigeons and small song birds often flew about the abandoned four story brick building at the corner of Chestnut and Worthington. I was hopeful that developers will bring life back to these vacant lots and abandoned buildings to help our neighborhood.

Throughout the day and night, I heard the sirens of the fire trucks as they left the station with flashing red lights, speeding to the scene of a fire. The police cruisers, from the police station two blocks east of my building, rushed with their sirens blaring and blue lights flashing as they were dispatched to emergencies. Each time I heard the fire, police or ambulance vehicles driving by I offered brief prayers for the safety and health of all involved. Two blocks to the north, the railroad passenger and freight trains rumbled and blew their horns as they travelled to and from the railroad station. And there were the constant sounds of trucks and cars, motorcycles, planes and helicopters which traversed the roads and the skies near my building. Other regular sounds were those of the patrons who walked by as they left the clubs and restaurants on the sidewalks of my neighborhood.

In the fall of 2014, Tony Bennett and Lady Gaga, two of my favorite singers released their jazz duet album **Cheek to Cheek.** Bennett, who had begun singing in New York City as a singing waiter was born Antonio Benedetto. He was given the new name of Tony Bennett by a friend to help his new career. He has continued as one of the greatest singers of this past century and this current century. I especially have enjoyed his friendship and musical collaboration with Lady Gaga, another New Yorker who changed her name from her original Italian, but has always honored her roots. She began her career as a classical and jazz pianist and soloist. The duets of Tony Bennett and Lady Gaga in recent years have reinvigorated both of their musical careers and my affection for both them.

Regularly I either walked or biked around the city, or used PVTA bus transportation. I owned a 10-speed Blackburn black bike with straight handlebars, no wheel guards, trail tires, and wire basket. I brought my bike into the McIntosh building and carried it upstairs in the elevator where I could keep it safe and secure. One time my bike had been stolen. The police let me see the video showing who had taken it. They knew me because I was active in the downtown neighborhood watch program. With all of the more important crimes under their jurisdiction, they were not able to search for one bike. One day about a month later I saw the person, who was attempting to sell my bike to someone for a good price. I stopped and said "I would be interested in buying this bike. But first can I take it for a spin to see if it is comfortable for me?" We were one block from the Police department on Pearl Street. I biked to the station and brought the bike into the lobby. I reported that this was my bike that had been stolen and asked if they would be able to go with me where I could point out the thief. I stayed out of sight and let them stop to talk with him. He was quite surprised when two officers confronted him with their information and were able to make the arrest. I was able to keep my bike. This was a good example of cooperation between the police and local citizens.

In 2015, I wrote a letter to the editor of **The Republican** about safety:

"In the grand scheme of world and national issues, safety on the streets and sidewalks in our local community may not appear to be significant. However, how we observe laws and rules of courtesy and common sense are crucial to our daily social lives.

"In most of the towns and cities of western Massachusetts, new and improved street and sidewalk planning, design and construction help keep us safe. Well marked street signs and lines, crosswalks and bikeways are important. As drivers, pedestrians and cyclists the laws and infrastructure are basic. However, each one of us bears the responsibility to know and follow the laws in order to protect our lives and those around us. The MassDOT signs that declare "Scan the Street" are important reminders of being alert to our surroundings at all times, whether we are the driver, pedestrian or cyclist.

"The bright white and yellow street markings, traffic lights and street signs all help us. Law enforcement personnel protect and serve all of us. But all the physical improvements are useless if we do not follow them every day. It only takes a moment of not being alert to cause injury, permanent disability or death. Distracted or impaired drivers, riders or pedestrians are the cause of many tragic accidents.

"For cyclists of every age I encourage reviewing the Massachusetts **Drivers Manual** from the Registry of Motor Vehicles and keeping abreast of other safety information will keep us informed for ourselves and those around us. Be a good citizen. Be safe."

At 64 years of age, I retired in the summer of 2016, having been employed by Peter Pan for forty years. Having relied on public transportation, biking and walking for most of my adult life, I purchased a pre-owned certified 2008 Mini Cooper so that I would have more independence in getting about. No longer needing to wear my Peter Pan uniform for work, most days I wore a neat pair of pants and a dress shirt. On special days I wore my one black suit and tie. I had worn this one suit for my wedding, for masses, for baptisms and funerals for more than forty years. With some minor alterations by a tailor, I could still fit in it. As I looked in the mirror, my face had gained wrinkles with age and my coal black wavy hair was now completely snow white. In the cold winter weather I wore a heavy grey long coat. At home, I wore jeans and sweat shirt.

I began collecting Social Security, health coverage through Medicare and a retirement pension from Peter Pan. It was an adjustment learning how to live on a limited fixed income. In retirement, I look forward to exploring more of New England and follow my own daily routine rather than have my free time determined by my driving schedule. I expect to continue many of the activities of my past and perhaps do some more exploring. I also plan to nurture my spiritual life with God, Jesus, the people and the natural world around me, practicing the social teachings of the Church. Some of these will include an awareness and advocacy about human trafficking, poverty, homelessness, hunger, climate change and peace and justice. The future of my life is an unknown mystery but I look forward to it with hope and a positive attitude.

JAMES PATERSON – MY LIFE AND ART

ALEXANDRIA, VIRGINIA AND SPRINGFIELD | 2011

As I prepared for my retirement, one of the traditions at American International College in Springfield, Massachusetts, was that faculty who were retiring were invited to present a lecture about their life and work or about a major topic that reflected their life. For that event, I wrote a talk to be presented before the faculty and friends on Commencement weekend. These reflections are developed from that lecture. After retirement I continued to add to it, which is still a work in progress. The sections of this story are mostly in chronological order.

My Childhood and Youth

My great-great-grandparents lived during the Civil War and Emancipation period, which covered 1843-1883. My great grandparents lived during Reconstruction and World War I, including 1870-1932. My grandparents lived during World War I and World War II, including 1900-1964. Several members of my family have spent considerable attention to tracing our ancestral roots and branches. I will leave to another time the results of their fascinating research.

My father was born in Alexandria in 1922 and died at the age of 61 in 1983. When my father was seventeen, Sam Tucker and several young African Americans, all friends of his, led a non-violent sit-down in 1939 at the Alexandria Library. The plan of the city was to build a library for the African Americans as an addition. But the sit-in urged the city to build Robinson Library as a separate building. My father served with the United States Army in Europe during World War II.

My mother was born in 1924 and died at the age of 70 in 1994, like my father, spending all of her life in Alexandria. The Parker-Gray School opened in 1920, providing an education for African American boys and girls in grades one through eight. The school was named for the late educator John Parker, Principal of the Snowden School for Boys, and Sarah Gray, Principal of the Hallowell School for Girls. For many years African American students had to travel to Washington, DC to receive an education beyond the eighth grade. Parker-Gray's first four-year high school class graduated in 1936.

I was born in 1947 in Alexandria, Virginia, an historic city which borders Washington, D.C., to the north. The city has always been closely involved with colonial and Federal history and national affairs. I grew up in "The Hill" neighborhood in the southern part of the city just west of the waterfront. My brothers and sisters all worked in construction in our family business.

From my parents and my teachers in the public schools of Alexandria, I learned about the history of African Americans in the city and the nation and about the rich heritage of the peoples and civilizations of Africa.

In 1790, when the first Federal census was taken, 52 free blacks were recorded as living in Alexandria. This population increased dramatically to 836 by 1810 and continued to expand until Alexandria retroceded to the Commonwealth of Virginia from the District of Columbia. By 1870 the black population reached 5,300. The earliest free black neighborhoods in the city began between 1790 and 1810. These neighborhoods were called "The Bottoms", "Hayti", "Uptown" and "The Berg". Four new black neighborhoods developed in the post-bellum period: "The Hill", "Cross Canal", "The Hump", and "Colored Rosemont."

The Market Square has been the center of the city since its founding in 1749. The Fairfax County Courthouse has also been located there since that time and local farmers often came to the square to sell produce. Slave exporters in Alexandria were leaders in the long-distance slave trade and the square was used as a slave market.

According to the Trans-Atlantic Slave Trade Database, between 1525 and 1866, 12.5 million Africans were shipped to the New World. Some

10.7 million survived the dreaded Middle Passage, disembarking in North America, the Caribbean, and South America. Of these survivors, only about 388,000 were shipped directly to North America. It is estimated that another 60,000 to 70,000 survivors ended up in the United States after touching down in the Caribbean first. This means that approximately 450,000 Africans arrived in the United States over the course of the slave trade. Most of the 42 million members of the current African American community descend from this group of less than half a million Africans.

The second phase of forced migration, known as the domestic or internal slave trade, involved two and a half times the number of black people who were taken from Africa to the United States. In the seven decades between the ratification of the Constitution in 1787 and the Civil War, approximately one million enslaved people were relocated from the upper South to the lower South, two thirds of these through the domestic slave trade. Owners in the upper South, whose tobacco plantations were no longer sufficiently profitable, sold them south in droves. The enormity of the second Middle Passage was due to the unprecedented growth of the cotton industry and the invention of the cotton gin by Eli Whitney patented in 1794. Before the cotton gin, one person could clean about a pound of cotton a day; but using the cotton gin, one person could clean fifty pounds a day. In 1790, the United States produced 1.5 million pounds of cotton a day. By 1860, on the eve of the Civil War, production of cotton had grown to 2,275 million pounds a day.

The historian Ira Berlin observed, "The internal slave trade became the largest enterprise in the South outside of the plantation itself, and probably the most advanced in its employment of modern transportation, finance, and publicity." As a result, the slave populations of Alabama, Mississippi, Arkansas and Texas swelled along with the value of slaves. Henry Louis Gates wrote "Of the 32 million slaves working in the fifteen slave states in 1850, 1.8 million worked in cotton. Cotton produced by slave labor was so profitable that it would take a costly civil war, and the loss of more than 600,000 lives, to end it."

In 1828, Isaac Franklin and John Armfield leased a three-story brick building on Duke Street to be used as a "Negro Jail" or slave pen for slaves being shipped from Northern Virginia to Louisiana. Active until 1836, this was one of the largest slave trading companies in the country, exporting over 3,750 slaves to the new cotton and sugar plantations of the Deep South. During the Civil War the building and its surrounding site were used as a military prison for deserters, the L'Ouverture Hospital for black soldiers and the barracks for contraband-slaves who fled the Confederate States and sought refuge with Union troops in Alexandria.

Among the prominent local citizens, Dr. Albert Johnson (1866-1949) lived on Duke Street and was one of the earliest professionally trained African American physicians to practice in Alexandria. He graduated in 1892 from Howard University Medical School, the first African American medical school.

During my childhood and youth, I attended the Roberts Memorial United Methodist Church in Alexandria, the oldest African American church building in the city. Roberts Chapel began as part of the predominantly white congregation at the First Methodist Episcopal Church in Chapel Alley. In 1830, four white and five black members purchased a lot and began the foundation for a separate church. Work stopped in 1831 because of the reaction to the Nat Turner Rebellion. The congregation was forced to move to the present site in 1834. Many of the African American worshippers came from the nearby community of Hayti, named for the country of Haiti, along one block of South Royal Street. Haiti was the first successful slave revolution in the western hemisphere. The residents of this block were whites and free blacks, many of whom had settled here after the American Revolution. Sometimes enslaved people lived with free black families. My parents and grandparents had also been members of Roberts Memorial UM Church. At this church, I learned the basics of faith: love, respect, traditional values, compassion and mercy, and was active in the civil rights movement and desegregation.

My High School, College and Early Adult Years

In 1950, because of increased enrollment at Parker-Gray School, a new school was built on Madison Street to house all the students. The school that remained on Whyte Street was renamed Charles Houston Elementary School. As result of integration, Parker-Gray High School was phased out and became a middle school from 1965 to 1979. The elementary school burned down and the site later became the home of the Charles Houston Recreation Center. In the 1960s, T.C. Williams High School, a new integrated school was built, which is where Jean and I attended high school.

Jean graduated from District of Columbia Teachers College in 1969 with a B.S. in Occupational Therapy. This college had been founded in 1851 as Normal School for Colored Girls and then merged to become District of Columbia Teachers College in 1955, the district's only land grant university. In 1977, it merged again to become the University of the District of Columbia.

I had graduated in 1968 from Howard University with a B.A. as an art and architecture major. Howard was one of the first Freedman's schools created after the Civil War for freed slaves and their descendants. Jean and I were descendants of escaped and freed slaves. Our great-great-grandparents and their children had lived in Virginia, through the Civil War and the time of Emancipation.

At Howard, one of my early African American heroes was Benjamin Banneker who had been born in Baltimore in 1731 and became a notable inventor, mathematician, astronomer and surveyor. When the decision was made to move the capital of the United States from Philadelphia to Washington, D.C., in 1791, Banneker, on the recommendation of Thomas Jefferson, was appointed to the civil engineering team planning the layout of the new city. Though almost sixty years old and in poor health, Banneker spent much time compiling data and maintaining the team's field astronomical clock. He helped determine the sites for the White House, the Capitol, the Treasury and other buildings.

Also, while at Howard, I studied the work of Henry Ossawa Tanner (1859-1937), who had studied for two years at the Pennsylvania Academy of Fine Arts. In 1891, Tanner went to Europe and enrolled at the *Academie Julian* in Paris under Jean-Joseph Benjamin-Constant. Two of his most famous paintings were **The Battle of Life** and **The Banjo Lesson** and many works on Biblical themes.

Some of the other African American artists of the 20th century whom I studied about were Aaron Douglas, Richmond Barthe, Archibald Motley, Palmer C. Hayden, Augusta Savage, Malvin Gray Johnson, W.H. Johnson, Hale A. Woodruff, Sargent Johnson, Charles H. Alston, Eldzier Cortor, Beauford Delaney, Joseph Delaney, Jacob Lawrence, Norman Lewis, Hughie Lee-Smith, Ellis Wilson, William Edmondson, Horace Pippin, Charles White, Elizabeth Catlett, John T. Biggers, Carroll H. Simms, Aloma W.Thomas, Ed Wilson, James W. Washington, Jr., and Richard Mayhew. Later during my career I developed a course about all of these artists of the 20th century which I taught both at Howard as a guest lecturer and in Springfield at the American International College.

I learned about the work of two architects Julian Francis Abele (1881-1950) and Paul Revere Williams (1894-1980). Abele joined the architecture firm of Horace Trumbauer, the leading architect in Philadelphia, and became the chief designer of major projects, including the Institute of Fine Arts at New York University, Harvard's Widener Library, much of Duke University, and the Philadelphia Museum of Art. Paul Revere Williams opened his own architectural firm in Los Angeles in 1923. In 1926, he became the first African American member of the American Institute of Architects.

The emergence of art departments in African American colleges and universities was significant in emphasizing art as an important subject of study but also as a means of livelihood for many artists employed as teachers. Research and learning about African and African American art has expanded and highlighted the heritage of African and African American art over many centuries.

At Howard University, there were three predominant African American art faculty members who have deeply influenced my education and career plus that of thousands of other graduates. These are James A. Porter, Lois Mailou Jones, and James Lesene Wells. In my career as an artist and architect I stand on the shoulders of these giants.

James A. Porter (1905-1970) was a pioneer of early black artists in America with his **Modern Negro Art,** published in 1943. Alongside his teaching, historical research and administrative duties as head of the Howard art department, he continued painting and exhibited his own work regularly. Lois Mailou Jones (1905-) taught at Howard for forty-seven years and was honored by a retrospective exhibition in 1989 at the Howard University Gallery of Art. The show demonstrated her transition from an academic painter to a modern, flat abstractionist whose later work reflected her knowledge of African symbols and artifacts. James Lesesne Wells (1902-1993) taught graphic design for many years at Howard. In addition to teaching, he was an excellent painter and printmaker. He was an American pioneer in the use of color in prints and a master of the fine white-line woodcut. He was also one of the first African American artists to find in African art concepts to simplify his own forms. He retired from Howard in 1968 and continued to paint and make prints into his eighties.

Having known each other as students, in 1968 Jean and I were married at the Roberts Memorial United Methodist Church in Alexandria and settled into the house that was built by my father and his brothers. This was a free standing wooden and brick two story house on North Patrick Street in a neighborhood with many row town houses.

Several of my ancestors were free black carpenters and brick masons who helped to build many of the houses in Alexandria. My father and two of his brothers built the house that they lived in. I grew up in one of those houses and after my parents died I inherited the house and lived in it with my wife and daughter. As a youth I loved to draw, especially houses and other buildings. This drawing ability led me to study art and architecture at Howard and become an artist and architect. I had a studio in our house. After our daughter Alyssa was born in 1973, we remodeled my home studio into her nursery and later her bedroom.

My father and two of his brothers formed the Paterson Company as a partnership to design and construct residential and commercial buildings. As their reputation grew along with the development of Alexandria, they also became involved in restoring some of the older buildings. I joined their company as the in-house architect. For all of my career I stayed on working with them, alongside my private creative art business.

The day after Armistice Day and the end of World War I, November 12, 1918, the U.S. Navy began constructing the U.S. Naval Torpedo Station. The factory built torpedoes for five years before becoming a storage building for munitions. With the onset of WWII, the Factory produced Mark III torpedoes for aircraft and Mark IV torpedoes for submarines. By the end of the war in 1945, the complex was converted to government storage for collections such as congressional documents, artifacts from The Smithsonian and Nazi trial records. The city of Alexandria bought the building in 1969. My maternal grandfather and grandmother had worked in the Torpedo Factory constructing the torpedoes during World War II. After the war my grandfather continued working there as a security guard.

In 1974 the Art League, a group of visionary artists, proposed to renovate part of the neglected factory into usable studio spaces. The Torpedo Factory Art Center became one of the country's earliest examples of creative reuse of industrial space. In 1976, I opened a private commercial art studio in the brand new Torpedo Factory Art Center and continued to specialize in drawing buildings for architects and commercial clients.

That project became a catalyst for the revitalization of the Potomac riverfront and the historic preservation of Old Town Alexandria as a thriving visitor destination. The dedication to converting a neglected industrial complex into the bright, inviting space it is today continues to be a prototype for other arts organizations around the world. The Torpedo Factory Art Center in 2017 is home to the largest number of publicly accessible working artists studios in the U.S. There are more than 160 resident artists in 82 working studios and six galleries, open daily to the public.

Our daughter Alyssa attended Alexandria schools from first through 12th grades. She attended Howard University and lived on campus for the four years until her graduation with an art and education double major in 1994. After graduation she joined me in my art studio and gallery in the Torpedo Factory Art Center. Her full-time work was as an art teacher serving the public elementary schools in Alexandria. At Howard, Alyssa became a member of Alpha Kappa Alpha. The oldest sorority of the Divine Nine-the historically black sororities and fraternities that make up the National Pan-Hellenic Council, Alpha Kappa Alpha was born in 1908 at Howard University as the first Greek letter sorority founded by African American college-educated women. AKA prides itself on supporting members' personal and professional development, advocating for social change and being of service to all mankind. It has grown into a global sisterhood with more than 290,000 members around the world.

In 1983, Jean and I participated with the Alumni Association of Parker-Gray School and the Alexandria Society for the Preservation of Black Heritage when together both groups reopened the building of the Robinson Library, the first public library to serve the African American population of Alexandria, as the Alexandria Black History Resource Center.

On a personal note, as I was allergic to cats and dogs, our pets at home were limited. Most of the time living in Alexandria, we had a fresh water aquarium in our living room. For many years until college, Alyssa kept some reptiles and amphibians in a glass tank in her bedroom. She especially enjoyed having turtles and iguanas. Her favorite subjects in school were biology and the visual arts. She also enjoyed drawing, especially wild animals in their native habitat.

Of all the Smithsonian museums in Washington, her favorites were the Museum of Natural History and the National Gallery of Art. Washington, D.C. is a half hour drive from Alexandria across one of the bridges across the Potomac River or a short ride on the Metro.

Our family enjoyed visiting some of the major tourist attractions in Alexandria which were open to the public and regularly had educational programs or events of interest to children and parents. Some of our favorites were the Carlyle House Historic Park, Gadsby's Tavern Museum, Lee-Fendall House Museum and Garden, Stabler-Leadbeater Apothecary Museum and The Lyceum: Alexandria's History Museum.

Our family of three was very close and had a pleasant and satisfying life together through the years. Our lives were entwined in activities and interests of school, work and church within an active city. We ate at home as much as possible, sharing in the cooking and household responsibilities. We were friends with most of our neighbors and engaged regularly in neighborhood events. We started with sharing one car, but eventually had to own two cars, and used public transportation as much as possible. We walked a lot within the city throughout all the seasons.

The Springfield Years- to Retirement 1994-2012

In early 1994, Alvin Paige, the Artist in Residence at American International College in Springfield, Massachusetts, recommended that I consider applying to work on the faculty. All of our lives Jean and I had lived in Alexandria. After much discussion, we decided to accept the position to teach for one year. Up to that time Jean had been busy raising Alyssa and taking care of our home in Alexandria.

In May 1994, Alyssa graduated from Howard University, my alma mater. She moved back into our Alexandria home to live there. We left most of our furniture in the house for her. She began teaching art full-time in the Alexandria elementary schools. She opened her own artist's studio in the space I had used as a studio and gallery in the Torpedo Factory Art Center. Alyssa and I began a professional collaboration as I left much of my creative art work with her to display and sell in her gallery. Most of my work consisted of pen and ink drawings of residences, commercial and public buildings in Alexandria and northern Virginia. As she was just beginning to develop her own portfolio of work, this provided her with a greater inventory to sell. She continued her interest in painting natural scenes and landscapes, as well as painting domestic and exotic animals, usually on commission with local residents and tourists. Fortunately, Alyssa had not inherited my allergies to domestic pets.

Due to Alyssa's teaching career, preparation time and class time, her periods of personal creative work were limited. She began entering her work in area art shows and becoming recognized for her work. However, for many years she depended on the income from teaching. Fortunately, we had paid off the mortgage on the house many years before so her housing expenses were minimal. During vacation times, especially during the long summer break, we returned to our own bedroom and visited with her. As an adult, Alyssa often dressed fashionably highlighting her curly long black hair with black fur trim coat, black riding pants, knee high black boots.

For the first academic year in Springfield, Jean and I rented an apartment and later searched for a house to purchase for a longer period. Another factor in our consideration of staying longer in Massachusetts was based on the option of returning to Alexandria to be closer to Alyssa since she was living and working there. Jean took graduate courses and received a Master of Science in Occupational Therapy (MSOT) from AIC.

In the 1830's for one hundred years, many French-Canadians immigrated to Springfield due to economic depression and food shortages in Canada. Many came to work for seasonal farm work or to work in the textile mills, settling in Indian Orchard, the South and North ends of Springfield, Chicopee and Holyoke. In contrast to the more unified geographic settlements of the Irish and Italians, the French-speaking community settled in dispersed areas. Millowners sent agents to bring back French-Canadians who would frequently work for less wages, and often did not participate in labor disputes. Like previous immigrant groups, the French-speaking residents developed institutions to maintain their French language, Catholic faith through churches and parochial schools and cultural traditions.

In 1888, the French Protestant College began in Springfield in the neighborhood now called Mason Square. By 1894 it changed its name to the French-American College and then in 1905 to American International College (AIC). Originally its primary student body consisted of immigrant students but it soon came to serve people of all backgrounds. Eventually, many of the French-Canadians improved their economic status, moving upward to become skilled workers and industrial leaders. Over the years, the AIC campus expanded to cover many blocks beyond its first buildings along Wilbraham Road and State Street.

The Karen Sprague Center for the Performing Arts was built to bring together programs in the visual and performing arts. In front of the center is a prominent Classical art installation consisting of several blocks from a fluted column with an Ionic capital from an ancient Greek building. Alvin Paige had been one of the leaders in the development of the center. Across the street was the house where Alvin maintained his office and studio.

In the spring of 1995, I accepted a longer contract teaching at AIC. Jean and I bought and moved to a house on Beech Street in the Mason Square and Watershops Pond area, near the AIC and Springfield College campuses. This house would become our home for the next seventeen years. It was a wooden-frame two-story house wrapped with white vinyl siding. The first floor had a small front porch and the top floor was an attic with gables. A short driveway along the side of the house ended at the garage in the small back yard.

Jean worked in a Springfield nursing home as an Occupational Therapist. I continued to teach art as an adjunct faculty member at AIC and create art in my art studio in our home. I gave or sold my work to the Springfield Museums and to individual customers. I was a consultant to the Quadrangle, especially with its two art museums and the science museum, featuring exhibits about Africa and African American history.

Alvin Paige and I collaborated and began to learn about each other's interests and talents. Because we worked in different media our interests and skills balanced each other. Alvin's methods included easel painting, sculpture, three dimensional forms, and installation art, mostly with media of bronze, plaster, resin, mixed-media and multi-media. His subjects were architecture images, buildings, churches and /or houses relating to social commentary, cultural and political views. Being African Americans from the South, Alvin and I shared the same racial ethnicity. He had left his business career in Hartford as a real estate broker and design consultant to work in Springfield as an artist. He was a distinguished looking man with curly grey hair, a moustache and small beard and expressive eyes.

Alvin Paige created a major outdoor art installation "Children of Sorrow" on the green of the Springfield Museums Quadrangle for the month of June 1995. Inside a 60-foot-long Quonset Hut, used during World War II to store munitions, Paige erected a shrine to the young victims of domestic and other forms of violence. Over one hundred and fifty 4-foot-tall white-shrouded illuminated figures, their eyes and forehead a black void facing the entrance, stood in rows like human tombstones within the hut. The foreshortened figures stood shoulder to shoulder, illuminated by a soft inner light from rings of glowing blue neon lights that encircle their feet. Formed from cast clay masks and monk-like robes which Paige molded over adolescent boys, the spectral figures represented life without hope and invoked the presence of young people who have died in violence.

Welded and imbedded in the wall were decommissioned guns which actually had been used in crimes. Other walls were plastered with collages of newspaper and magazine stories about youth violence and its effects on families, neighborhoods and cities, all collected by Paige over the years. A large video screen scrolled down the names of actual slain children along with images selected and edited by the artist. His work was meant to memorialize all children who had died from guns, weapons and/or drugs. More than 45,000 children and teenagers had been killed by guns alone between 1979-1995 in the United States, according to the Children's Defense Fund. He had lectured and exhibited internationally, including major shows in Ireland, Japan, and four cities within the People's Republic of China. He said "Art is important as medium that can say things that other forms of communication can't. It can speak to people from both sides of a social situation, and get people to understand. "

Paige said "You come here in the park to get away from all the things that are wrong in the world, and suddenly you're confronted with it. Maybe you should be uncomfortable. People don't like to be reminded of the bad things we've done in this world." The display was initially commissioned by the Springfield Fine Arts Museum and American International College and made possible by donations from many individuals and organizations.

About 40 National Guard troops helped dig out the abandoned dirt-encrusted shelters, 60 feet long by 20 feet wide by 18 feet high, from a World War II military reserve base at Camp Edwards on Cape Cod. Dozens of other soldiers, metal workers, carpenters, students and teachers lent a hand in building the rest of the exhibit. Paige, earlier in his career, had used public sites for oversized statements: a 30-foot stylized statue of Christ at a military camp, a Zulu Warrior at the Boston Museum of Fine Arts, a human figure in a wheelchair at the United Nations in New York City.

This project began in a school paper he wrote about handgun control. College-trained with degrees both in business management and art, he began thinking about the potential for spiritual and artistic symbolism in circles like the rounded shape of the Quonset hut. Paige wrote, "If art has a purpose, it's to go against the grain- to illustrate that the norm is not always correct. My art presents a picture- a slice of life as it is- which can sensitize people to action. When I started writing about crime and violence 19 years ago, it was about terrorism and social and political crimes and violence. It has come down to our own people killing our own people- children killing children. We're losing our next generation of leaders."

African Americans in Springfield

Now, I want to share some of the history of the African Americans and the Mason Square neighborhood of Springfield. In the 1700's many African Americans gained freedom from slavery by their service in the Continental Army during the War of Independence. Others sought freedom through legal suits and the determination of equal rights under the United States Constitution adopted in 1787. The Fugitive Slave Law abrogated the effect of the Constitution because it required that escaped slaves must be returned to their masters.

Jenny, a fugitive slave arrived and settled in Springfield. Soon afterwards her owner arrived from New York to claim his property and take her back with him. In her defense, the town selectmen and several local citizens purchased Jenny from her owner and then freed her. As a freedwoman, Jenny remained a resident in the Mason Square area. In 1808, she became the last slave to be freed in the town.

The Underground Railroad was the response of many Americans to enable slaves to escape to freedom into the northern states and Canada. Springfield was on the route and one of major way stations of this clandestine network. About 1840, several fugitives decided to risk capture and settle in Springfield. At first most African Americans were restricted to the Cross and Willow Street and Hancock Street and Eastern Avenue areas. The first church for African Americans was the Free Church Zion Methodist Church which began on Sanford Street near Main Street in the oldest area of the city. Later Free Church became St. John's Congregational Church now located on Hancock Street.

Although African Americans were allowed to worship with whites in the earlier churches, prejudice and hostility often discouraged interracial fellowship. In 1844 there were about one hundred and fifty African Americans in the town. From the churches as a base, self-help and self-protection groups to aid the minority population were organized.

With the development of more factories and mills, new residential areas were created near the Watershops Pond and the Ames Paper Mills. The first Methodist Church, called Asbury Chapel, was built on Hickory Street. By 1820, the population of Springfield was 3,914 people. Fifty-eight percent of those employed in the city in that year were in manufacturing, working mainly at the Armory, Ames Paper Mills and Belcher's Iron Works. These workers settled into growing neighborhoods in the North End, but most settled on Armory Hill and along Mill River in the South End. The population grew rapidly in response to many industrial and commercial opportunities as the town developed as a transportation crossroads and the town became a city in 1852.

By 1860 two hundred and seventy-six African Americans lived in the city. Many African Americans served in the military during the Civil War. There were approximately fifty-seven African American men living in the city in 1863 between the ages of 16 and 45, at least half of whom enlisted in the Union Army.

Following the Civil War and the emancipation of slaves in the South, many emigrated to settle in the North, a trend which continued for many years. In 1899, Rev. Dr. William Nelson DeBerry arrived to become pastor of St. John's Congregational Church. Some of the other African American religious organizations started in the 1840's. These included Zion Methodist Church in 1844 on Sanford Street and Bethel African Methodist Episcopal Church in 1849 on Loring Street. The Quincy Street Mission Sunday School developed into the St. John's Congregational Church which merged with the Sanford Street Church.

During the Civil War, the economy of the city prospered largely due to the Federal government contracts for guns and ammunition being produced at the Federal Armory. When Fort Sumter was attacked in 1861, one thousand guns per month were being produced in Springfield; by 1864, the rate was one thousand guns per day. Three thousand, four hundred workers were employed at the Armory. Third Baptist Church, serving the African American community, began in 1870. In the last two decades of the nineteenth century, many new churches and synagogues were started to serve the rapidly growing population of Catholics, Protestants and Jews. In 1899 Wesley Methodist Episcopal Church began on State Street.

Twenty-five hundred men from Springfield joined the military troops to fight in the Union Army against the Southern Confederacy. In 1888, the French Protestant College started, having begun a few years earlier in Lowell, Massachusetts, to serve the French-speaking population. During the twentieth century, the city and its population were affected by the major events of the First World War, he Great Depression of 1929, the Second World War, the Korean Conflict, the civil rights movement and the Vietnam War. The ethnic and national diversity of the city continued to expand with significant populations of English, Irish, Italian, French Canadian, Russian, German, Swedish, Polish, Greek, Syrian, Turkish, Puerto Rican, many Spanish -speaking countries and Vietnamese.

Following the Second World War, migration of African Americans from the South, in order to find better employment, housing and educational opportunities, led to a larger community in the city. The status of many families began to improve although discrimination and prejudice also continued.

Activities with Wesley United Methodist Church and the Quadrangle

Since I had been active in the United Methodist Church in Alexandria, it was a natural decision for Jean and me to become members of Wesley United Methodist Church on State Street in Mason Square. There were some programs which I had presented in Alexandria, that I offered to present in Wesley. Many of them were illustrated lectures which I had still available among my personal belongings.

Over the years in Springfield here are some of the programs that I presented both at Wesley and at a few other churches. In Advent, I gave a series on the portrayals of Mary and Jesus as an infant both throughout European art and in other cultures of the world. In Lent I provided a similar program on portrayals of the life of Jesus, and especially during the Passion of the last week of his life, from European and international art. These series were helpful for African Americans to learn that the presentation of Jesus in art is developed from the different cultures. Much of classical European art was done by Caucasian artists in predominantly Caucasian areas. My teaching showed that artists of many other areas of the world created Jesus and his times with diverse perspectives.

I also presented a series of sermons on Christian faith and the arts which gave Biblical and theological background to the value of the fine arts and performing arts within the context of belief and practice. These sermons included subjects such as: Beauty, Quilting, Poetry, Music, Visual Arts, Drama, Fiction and Film. I also organized tours and partnerships with other religious congregations or houses of worship in Springfield, and within the Mason Square area. For over ten years, I presented these programs in early fall or late spring.

Each year I identified a small group of selected congregations that we studied with and shared exchange visits so we learned about each other as neighbors, dealing with the history, beliefs and practices, worship, art and architecture of each faith community. At the time of my working in Springfield, there were over twenty-five such congregations in Mason Square, most of which were African American majority communities. Some of these annual events led to long-lasting relationships among several of the faith communities and our Wesley United Methodist Church members and leaders. All of these programs related to several of my academic courses at AIC and my professional career as a teacher, artist and architect.

I presented several lectures at the Quadrangle in their Museums a la Carte series, often based on my courses or on works displayed in the museums. The Quadrangle collections provided many objects and works and themes for these lectures, slides or later developed as Power Point presentations: Islamic, ancient Greek, Ancient Roman, American, Medieval, Renaissance, Modern periods.

Some of the favorite works upon which I gave lectures at the Quadrangle or incorporated in my AIC courses included the following, with reference to each work's location in the museums:

Museum of Fine Arts- Late Medieval gallery: "The Procession to Mount Gargano" by Nicolas Frances; Northern European and Italian Renaissance: "Bacchus and Ariadne" by Allesandro Turchi (called Veronese); Channing Blake Gallery- "Allegory of Architecture" by Francesco Trevisani; Friedmann Gallery-" Italian Landscape with Ruins" by Pierre Patel, the Elder; "Portrait of a Married Couple" by Jacques Dumont; 17th century Dutch-" Fishing Boats Offshore in a Calm" by Willem van de Velde; 18th century Italian "Madonna and Child" by Giovanni Battista Tiepolo; 19th century French- "Ophelia" by Jules Joseph Lefebvre; Leary Gallery- "Portrait of Eugene Murer" by Camille Pissarro; "Le Seine" by

Maximilien Luce; "The Net Mender" by George Newell Bowers. Modern & Contemporary gallery- "Fall from Grace" by Arnaldo Roche-Rabell; "Cave" by Helen Frankenthaler; "Then the Water Came and Quenched the Fire" by Frank Stella, Early 20th Century American Gallery- "New Mexican Landscape" by Georgia O'Keeffe.

George Walter Vincent Smith Art Museum- The Grand Tour- Assorted vases; Classical Cast Gallery- "Aphrodite" American Paintings Salon: "Landscape" by Robert W. Van Boskerck, "Autumn Woods: Road to Ausable Ponds, Adirondacks" by Roswell Morse Shurtleff; "Hamburg Cove" by William Chadwick; "Sunrise in the Hetch Hetchy Valley, California" by Albert Bierstadt; "Still Life with Ginger Jar, Pumpkin and Samovar" by William Merritt Chase. Chinese cloissone gallery, Japanese decorative arts, Chinese Porcelain gallery, Japanese bronzes; Islamic World "Prayer Rug".

In the Phelon African Hall at the Quadrangle an entire wall includes photos and brief descriptions of each of the annual Ubora Award recipients. Several of these awardees became friends of mine during my time in Springfield. Especially these included (with the date of their award in parentheses): Josephine Edmonds supporter of black artists (1998), Ronald Harrell, Harrell Funeral Home (2005), Zee Johnson (Olive Tree Books-n-Voices, Hancock Street (2010), Al and Gerry Garner (2011) and Robert and Katie Glasgow (2013) First Church UCC, Longmeadow.

* * *

Here are some Inspiring and wise quotations by African Americans which I regularly found helpful in my life, but also as words for my students.

"When you clench your fist, no one can put anything in your hand." Alex Haley, American writer

"Never confuse knowledge with wisdom. By wisdom I mean wrestling with how you live." Cornel West, American activist and philosopher

"The ultimate measure of a man is not where he stands in moments of comfort and convenience, but where he stands at times of challenge and controversy." "Don't hate- it's too big a burden to bear." Martin Luther King, Jr, Civil rights leader

"It is better to look ahead and prepare than to look back and regret." Jackie Joyner-Kersee, American Olympic heptathlete

"The more you praise and celebrate your life, the more there is in life to celebrate." Oprah Winfrey, actress, humanitarian, producer

"The thing that I have done throughout my life, is to do the best job that I can, to be me." Mae C. Jemison, American astronaut

"Excellence is not an act but a habit. The things you do the most are the things you do the best."

Marva Collins, American educator

"If there is no struggle, there is no progress." Frederick Douglass, American abolitionist, writer

"The arc of the moral universe is long, but it bends towards justice." Theodore Parker, American abolitionist

"...though it is sometimes very difficult to imagine our nation totally free of racism and sexism, my intellect, my heart and my experience tell me that it is actually possible. For that day when neither exists we must all struggle." James Baldwin, American writer

"Our lives, hopes and dreams depend on our ability to be heard." James Bernard, American writer

"Gray skies are just clouds passing over." Duke Ellington, American composer

"Hope is a song in a weary throat." Pauli Murray, American lawyer and minister

"All you need in the world is love and laughter. That's all anybody needs. To have love in one hand and laughter in the other." August Wilson, American playwright

* * *

Most of the times when I was working in my studio, I preferred to play background music to inspire me, usually classical composers from the Age of the Baroque through the age of classicism, the Romantic age and the Age of Modernism. Among my favorite composers were Handel, Bach, Scarlatti, Haydn, Mozart, Beethoven, Paganini, Rossini, Schubert, Berlioz, Mendelssohn, Chopin, Schumann, Liszt, Verdi, Bruckner, Brahms, Saint-Saens, Tchaikovsky, Dvorak, Grieg, Rimsky-Korsakov, Faure, Elgar, Debussy, Sibelius, Williams, Rachmaninoff, Ravel, Bartok, Stravinsky, Hindemith, Gershwin, Copland, Shostakovich and Britten.

Billie Holliday, Aretha Franklin, Eartha Kitt, LaVern Baker, Cab Calloway, B.B.King, Ray Charles, Duke Ellington, Ella Fitzgerald, Louis Armstrong, Lena Horne, Leontyne Price, Miles Davis, and John Coltrane were some of my favorite African American musicians. I enjoy music on any instrument, but my favorite instruments are piano, flute, violin, cello, horn, clarinet and the human voice.

My Heart Attack 2000

In late June of 2000, I had just finished the third mowing of my lawn for the season. I had a self-propelled gasoline rotary push mower. After the lawn was completely done, I went into my house to cool off. I felt a heavy pressure on my chest and first thought I was having indigestion. I told Jean what I was feeling. She immediately called 911 to request an ambulance. Within a few minutes the crew had arrived, checked my vital signs and declared that it appeared I was having a heart attack. They transported me quickly to Mercy Hospital on Carew Street in Springfield. My symptoms subsided once I was given oxygen and monitored. Upon arrival within ten minutes at the Mercy Hospital ER I was examined by their ER team. After a consultation with the hospital cardiologist and several tests over the next several hours, the doctor informed me that I needed emergency surgery which would be done early the next morning. With three arteries occluded no other option was left besides the open heart surgery with a triple coronary artery bypass. I completed all the admissions paper work. That evening I signed the consent form for open heart surgery. Jean and I read the list of all the possible medical events that could happen during and after the surgery, up to and including death. The conversations during the day emphasized that I was starting to have a myocardial infarction. Because I had come into the hospital so quickly, the heart muscles had not been damaged. However, I understood that this was very serious and that I could still die while in the hospital.

I had been informed the night before that the surgical operating room team would include a Muslim as primary surgeon, a Greek from Turkey as anesthesiologist, a surgical resident from England and the remainder of the staff of nurses and technicians being Jewish or Christian.

The morning of my surgery had arrived and I was first patient scheduled. The day of tests, waiting and apprehension were now past.

The heart machine had been charged with blood given by unknown persons. The interfaith team that surrounded me prompted me to offer this prayer for all those present and those loved ones waiting in the waiting area. Just before the anesthesia was administered, I prayed from the operating table these words that I had written down the night before:

"O God, by whatever Name we call you, we bring before you our aspirations, our hopes, our frustrations, our fears and indecisiveness. You whose creative powers are beyond our mental and physical grasp so many times, yet who has given us the inspiration always to move into new areas, be with us at this time as we touch body and soul to bring healing and wholeness. There is so much we do not fully understand, but You give us so much that we can grow into, to learn, and to understand.

"Give to all here present, from the least to the greatest, the knowledge of Your strength, Your purpose. Help us to remember that those who strive together in love and respect can change a life and a world.

"May that spirit of sharing together bring a renewed sense of appreciation, love and awareness of Your unity, wholeness and healing.

"Give to this servant the patience, the trust and the faith to rest in the care of these Your servants as Your instruments. There is no place we can go that is beyond Your care, Your protection and Your love.

Shalom, Salaam Aleichum, Ef Christo and may we all be with God. So be it! Amen."

In a few moments the anesthesia was administered. I was unaware of the rest of the day. Several hours later, gradually I could hear the sounds of machines and movement of people, but drifted in and out of consciousness. I responded groggily to someone telling me "the surgery is all over and all went well". All of this time I was in the recovery room. Regularly I was aware of a nurse who would check the monitor and the many tubes going into and out of various parts of my body and limbs. I was on my back most of the time, but regularly a nurse would turn me onto my side to pummel my back and upper chest. I knew that the pummeling was important to keep the lungs clear of fluid and to prevent further complications. I would often be asked "How are you feeling?" I replied most times "Lousy, like a truck ran over my entire body" or "Did an elephant sit on my chest?". I knew the major pain was where my sternum had been sawed open and my rib cage spread apart to allow the doctors to perform the surgery. The heart and lung machine had kept my blood and breathing going during the surgery.

I lost all track of time. Jean and Alyssa, separately, would come to stand by my bedside for only a few minutes each hour and then return to the waiting room. Eventually, I was moved into the CCU and was more alert but still tired and falling asleep often. The pain continued, although I was on constant pain medication. Fortunately for Alyssa, her vacation from teaching school had begun. She had been able to fly up from DC to Bradley. In the CCU the visits were still restricted to only Jean or Alyssa for very short periods. After several days I was moved from the CCU into a regular room to recover, still monitored by the nurses. Another major step was to get out of bed, first for only a few steps, then each time later I was permitted to walk further. First I walked only in the room and then to venture into the halls, as I slowly regained my strength and mobility.

Light food was first introduced and then the full meals on the hospital menu. The first few nights included weird dreams which then disappeared during the light of day. Fantasy shadows of the night disappeared and in the daylight I could realize I was in the hospital room. Eventually I could have other visitors beyond my family in the private room. I was awake much more of each day. Being able to walk in the halls, and check in with other cardiac patients showed me that life goes on as each one recovered and was discharged from the hospital.

I realized that all the tubes were uncomfortable, but I knew they were there for a purpose. Feeling pain meant that I was alive. The constant care by the nursing staff assured me that I was getting better. Everything they did was to help my recovery. The cardiologist came to visit with me when I was more alert and he gave me more assurance about the surgery and my future path to recovery. During this period, I recalled my gratitude for Dr. Charles Drew, (1904-1950) the African American surgeon and research scientist. Before World War II he had done research about the storage of blood. He invented the methods for large scale transfusion, storage and transportation of blood that saved the lives of thousands of British and American troops during the war. During my surgery, his inventions saved my life as well.

Over the next few days my bodily functions returned to normal and independence. The last tubes removed were those that drained the fluids from my chest during and after the surgery. The sounds of the monitors and the presence of the wires kept the staff aware of my signs every minute.

Then came the day the doctor informed me that I would be discharged and could go home! Jean and Alyssa drove me home where I could be back in my own bed. At first I was anxious not to have 24/7 nursing care and resources of the hospital. I would think about what if I have a medical problem. How would I know without the presence of monitors and staff? I learned to trust the loving care of my wife and daughter. The fact that Jean was a trained occupational therapist meant that she also had skills and knowledge to help me. The few weeks of bed-rest at home included being able to sit up for meals and to walk around inside and outside. I was informed how long I needed to be at home, and what my restrictions were. Then came the time I could go out for rides, but not to be the driver while the incision and bones were healing.

Next I started an outpatient cardiac rehabilitation program going to the center associated with the hospital. There I began physical therapy of exercising three days a week on a regular schedule. I steadily increased the use of the treadmill, the cycling machine and the rowing machine. The therapy was monitored by a nurse who checked my blood pressure and pulse at each visit. Besides the physical exercise, I also consulted with the staff about nutrition and other ways to take care of myself. Along with other cardiac patients doing their rehabilitation, I began to resume daily tasks at home and then returned to work, driving and a regular schedule after one month. Since my summer work schedule at AIC was light and students were on vacation, I was able to recover without disrupting my academic routine.

Jean was able to resume her work as an OT but she continued to be a great, loving support with experience dealing with patients and finding creative ways to develop my skills while regaining my strength. Of course, it was a natural area for me as the arts are integral to OT. For the rest of my life, I managed my health by taking medications, monitoring my daily menu, exercising regularly and seeing my doctors regularly. I was fortunate to have survived the heart attack and continue my daily life with care and moderation and live independently in my own home. I continued to have respect for those with different views and backgrounds. I enjoyed learning about each other's beliefs and practices and life experiences.

Alvin Paige's Retirement

Alvin Paige retired in January 2007. He retired from the position of Artist in Residence and the Director of Karen Sprague Cultural Arts Center and the Esther B. Griswold Theater for the Performing Arts at AIC. He had been employed on the administrative staff creating art and managing the design of several of the buildings on campus, especially the Karen Sprague Center. He was not a faculty member and did not teach classes. He was honored with a video documentary "Alvin Paige: The Retrospective, I Remember". He observed his 73rd birthday July 13, 2007 and was diagnosed with Alzheimer's Disease in 2018. For the next two years he lived at home or was a patient or resident in several different facilities, including McLean Continuing Care and the Fisher House in Amherst. Alvin died on October 8, 2010. A memorial service was held in the Esther B. Griswold Theater on October 30, including a screening of the Retrospective film and words of reflection by family and friends. Family burials were held at the Massachusetts Veterans' Memorial Cemetery in Agawam and in his birthplace, La Grange, Georgia. Donations were given in his memory to the Hospice of the Fisher Home in Amherst and the Children's Defense Fund.

During his hospital and residential care, I visited him as often as I could. It was difficult for me, and any of his family and friends, to see him become so dependent on the care of professionals and family members as the progressive disease affected his mind and memory. His personality remained kind and patient. Who he was as a person consisted of the close relationship between his imagination and mind and his creative ability to transform those ideas into art. As he gradually lost his ability to recognize his family members, and his ability to communicate verbally, he became a shell of himself. It was difficult to see him come to his last days of life and I valued greatly his legacy as a person, a friend and as an artist.

Jean's Stroke 2009

Jean and I lived on Beech Street together until 2009 when she died suddenly and peacefully in her sleep from a massive stroke. I discovered her still body when I awoke in the morning. She had not made any sounds or movements during the night that had awakened me. She had not had any previous signs of symptoms of circulation problems. Within a few minutes of my call to 911, the EMTs and police arrived. They informed me that there was nothing they or I could have done to save her.

Alyssa came up and within a week we held a memorial service at Wesley United Methodist Church where we had been members during our time in Springfield. Pastor Geraldine officiated at the service which included many of Jean's favorite hymns: *Abide with me; Lead, kindly Light; My Lord, what a mourning,* and *What a friend we have in Jesus.* The scripture readings included some of her personal favorites: Psalm 90, Psalm 145, Matthew 5:3-12 and Romans 8:18-39. The memorial service to remember her life and to release her soul into the care of God was for our Springfield friends and colleagues. Following the service, the women of the church provided a buffet lunch and time to visit with everyone. With the guidance and support of Henderson Funeral Home, we had decided to cremate her body and then have her cremains interred in Alexandria. Except for Alyssa, I had encouraged all of our family and friends in Alexandria to wait in the south until we would have a memorial service in Alexandria at a later date.

A month later I took her cremains to Alexandria where we had a second memorial service, very similar to the one we had had in Springfield. Her cremains were buried in the Alexandria National Cemetery, in a family plot including five generations of my family. Her family ancestors, also representing five generations, were buried about a hundred feet away from my direct ancestors. It was still an active place for burials. Freedmen's Cemetery was another historic cemetery for African Americans, off South Washington Street a few blocks away.

During the time of my grieving in the next two years, with Alyssa's help, I decided to downsize many of our possessions. When we came to Springfield, we had bought mostly new furniture. Our family heirlooms and original furniture had remained in the house in Alexandria where Alyssa had been living. Many of our photographs we transferred to digital files. We donated all of her clothing and other items to Goodwill and second hand shops. We had gathered and collected a lot of stuff while living in Springfield. I decided to remain in the same house, but with much cleared out. Much of what belonged to Jean, especially books and supplies for her Occupational Therapy work were useful to Alyssa for her own art work, and other objects would be useful for Alyssa's found art, collages and assemblages.

My teaching and work with art and architecture

In my teaching and work throughout my career, I have lifted up the work of African American artists. One of these is Elizabeth Catlett who was born in Washington, D.C. in 1919 and is acclaimed for her abstract sculptures, prints and paintings. In 1947 she produced her **I Am A Negro Woman** series of sculptures, prints and paintings. Her **Homage to My Young Black Sisters** (1968) celebrated strong black women and mothers which has been a consistent theme throughout her art. In 2003 she unveiled her monumental sculpture honoring the late author Ralph Ellison, commissioned by the City of New York and situated in Riverside Park in Harlem. She was a graduate of Howard University.

Carmen de Lavallade, dancer, actor and choreographer performed with many different dance and theatre companies. She once wrote "Art is so fantastic because the mind is so remarkable. We keep inventing new things; nothing is repeated. Human nature is that way. .. This would be a dead world without the arts. During the wars, (WWI and WWII) when we didn't have the arts, everything was dead. It is an absolute physiological, emotional necessity. I have seen people's lives changed because of the arts... Do the best you can with what you've got; be yourself."

Dolores Kendrick, poet and educator, was a native of Washington, D.C., and the author of **The Women of Plums: Poems in the Voices of Slave Women.** "I had imagination. I would write stories in school. I was so happy creating stories. I just loved to write. It made me happy to let my imagination go to all of these various and sundry places, and to conceive of things, and to make things happen in the corners of my mind, and to put it down on paper."

One of my favorite poets and songwriters was James Weldon Johnson. He and his brother wrote more than two hundred songs. He published a book of poetry **Fifty Years and Other Poems**. Johnson used his position as editor of NAACP's **Crisis** magazine to promote the work of African American writers and artists. One of his most well known and enduring songs is "Lift Every Voice and Sing."

* * *

Here are some other quotations which I often had posted on the walls of my classrooms. These were valuable in my own personal and professional life, but also as references for my students.

"Never be afraid to sit awhile and think." Lorraine Hansberry, American dramatist

"Living and dying is not the big issue. The big issue is what you're going to do with your time while you're here." Billy T. Jones, American dancer and choreographer

"All my work is meant to say, "You may encounter defeats, but you must not be defeated." Maya Angelou, American poet and writer

We are positively a unique people. Breathtaking people. Anything we do, we do big! Despite attempts to stereotype us, we are crazy, individual, and uncorralable people." "Be black, shine, aim high." Leontyne Price, American opera singer

"You've got to find a way to let people know you're there." Nikki Giovanni, American poet

"Don't give up trying to do what you really want to do. Where there's love and inspiration, I don't think you can go wrong." Ella Fitzgerald, American singer

"...though it is sometimes very difficult to imagine our nation totally free of racism and sexism, my intellect, my heart and my experience tell me that it is actually possible. For that day when neither exists we must all struggle." James Baldwin, American writer

"Gray skies are just clouds passing over." Duke Ellington, American composer

"All you need in the world is love and laughter. That's all anybody needs. To have love in one hand and laughter in the other." August Wilson, American playwright

* * *

Here are most of the courses that I taught most regularly over the seventeen years I was teaching at AIC: History of Art, Aesthetic Experience in the Contemporary Visual Arts, Art Appreciation Through Drawing, Art Appreciation Through Painting, Studio Painting, Craft and Design, Cultivating Creativity, The Vital Basics: Drawing, painting and Sculpture, Graphic design, and Art and Culture: A Global Look. Many of these courses also included field trips. An annual study abroad course was the Art of Rome and Florence. There were two adjunct faculty, me being one of them, who taught these courses. My colleague was Lauri, an art major graduate from Springfield College who had worked as an intern with Alvin Paige. As is true for most artists in any form of expression, one's career often consisted of cobbling together several jobs to maintain an acceptable income. I also taught several art courses for adults during the school year and summers at the Springfield Museums, which drew from several of these academic courses. Some of these short courses also included Public Art and Architecture in Springfield, Urban Sketching Workshop, Drawing and Painting Urban Buildings: Residential, Commercial and Public.

While I was in Springfield, I continued to work on assignments with The Paterson Company, our family construction and architectural firm in Alexandria, working from home on the computer, by phone or going back down to Virginia. The public transportation back and forth was excellent. If I flew, I travelled to and from Bradley International Airport and Reagan International Airport in Washington, D.C. If I went by rail, I travelled by Amtrak trains to and from Union Station in Springfield and Alexandria, Virginia.

During my time in Springfield, The Paterson Company had developed into a thriving family business with more than thirty employees in Virginia. Our advertising featured the following information: Architect, Planners, Contractors; Private and Public; Office Buildings; Commercial and Retail; Historic Renovation and Reuse; Multi Family and Condominiums; Custom Private Residences and Additions; Interiors. Founded by my father and his brothers, my second generation was now in leadership positions, including my brothers, sisters and myself. Nieces, nephews, cousins and partners by marriage keep joining along with those not family members.

The projects in Alexandria have consisted of the restoration of several of the public buildings, commercial buildings and residences which were historically important. The largest project that began while I was in Massachusetts was the new National Museum of African American History and Culture on the Washington Mall. Because of my prior connections with the Washington, D.C. area, I was a consultant and resource to the curator and the team planning the collection and displays.

The Tornado of June 1, 2011

On Wednesday, June 1, 2011, a sudden tornado swept through Springfield and area towns. That morning and afternoon the sky was clear and no signs of a storm coming. The weather forecast was that there would be rain and heavy winds later that day. I was at home in the afternoon and there were storms and heavy rain. I was inside reading when all of a sudden I heard the sound like a freight train and I looked out and saw large dark clouds and the hook of the cloud descending towards the ground. I could see debris spinning around in the hook and first did not recognize what it was. Then, I realized that it was swirling spout of a tornado. Immediately, I went down into the basement and crouched near the cement wall. The noise increased and I felt the air sucked out of my lungs and pressure in my whole body and head. I could hear sounds of ripping and tearing nearby and all above me in the house being thrown violently around. All of a sudden it became calm. At first I thought the tornado had passed by. But then I recalled similar stillness when I had experienced hurricanes. I felt that this might be the eye of the hurricane, or in this case the tornado, and that the swirling wind would resume. Sure enough, the sucking sound and terrible wrath began again. All this time I could also hear the heavy falling rain and the sounds of crashing outside. When it finally became calm I waited awhile before getting up and climbing the stairs into my kitchen. The wind had lessened and it continued to rain, the dark clouds move away and the sun was visible. Everything in my house had been broken and blown around. Half of my roof above the second floor was gone and the walls on one side of the house completely gone.

I went outside and saw damaged houses along both sides of Beech Street. Neighbors were coming out of their houses, gaping at all the damage and wandering around in shock. I began walking and checking with the people along the street. "Are you hurt?" "Is any one missing from your home?" I had my cell phone and began asking: "Do you need to call any one to let them know you are OK?" "Do you need any medical attention?" We realized that there was no electric power and landline telephones were not working.

Although it appeared that no one on our street needed emergency help, we could hear ambulance sirens all around us. There were no fires that had started in our neighborhood, but we could hear the sirens of police cars and fire trucks. Able bodied men and women began helping those who had boards of wood, fences or house siding and other debris scattered in their yards and the street. Those with cell phones were able to assist in communications with family members. One of the houses on our street had been lifted up and set back down on its foundation. Eventually, after several hours police began checking street by street to determine who needed help. Most of our houses were damaged, and some completely destroyed. We were advised to go and stay with friends or family who were in areas not hit by the tornado. For those who did not have somewhere to go, we were advised where emergency shelters were being set up. We were able to follow the news reports on our phones.

I learned that our church building was not damaged and that it would provide shelter for families and persons needing to go there. Across the street from the church, DeBerry School was also opened as a shelter. The local schools that were damaged were closed. Many of the undamaged schools were closed for classes but opened as emergency shelters. Along with some of the men on our street, I volunteered to stay overnight in a few of the houses which were safe to enter in order to provide security.

At 11:00 p.m., Wednesday evening, we listened to a press conference which provided the first comprehensive official report. Those speaking at Raymond Sullivan Safety Complex of the Springfield Fire Department declared a State of Emergency for the entire path of the tornado. Senator John Kerry, Governor Deval Patrick, Mayor Dominic Sarno and many other city and county officials were present. "At 4:17 pm on Wednesday, June 1, the first tornado touched down in Westfield and it wreaked havoc for the next one hour and ten minutes as the path continued through Agawam, West Springfield, Springfield, Wilbraham, Monson, Brimfield, Sturbridge, and ended at the Sturbridge-Charlton townline at 5:27 pm. 350 homes and businesses were destroyed and more than 1,500 buildings damaged by three distinct tornadoes, one major and two minor, in those communities."

"Within the city boundaries, the storm continued through the heart of the city, up Central Street to the Springfield College campus and over Watershops Pond into the East Forest Park neighborhood where it leveled several homes. By the time it exited Springfield from Tinkham Road to Sixteen Acres it had damaged many buildings."

The next morning, Thursday, June 2, the huge front page headline of **The Republican** declared "DEVASTATION", with several pages of stories about the destruction caused by the three tornadoes. All of the next day I stayed to help people with incoming and outgoing phone calls and removing debris, and helping our neighbors who were disabled or elderly. In the course of Thursday and Friday, police officers and firefighters checked every house to take a census of the status of each house and family.

Representatives of other municipal departments checked house by house as to which houses needed to be condemned and demolished and which could be repaired. My house was certified as habitable once the roof and wall was repaired, unless further inspections revealed more structural damage. All of my bedroom and my art studio was spared damage from the wind and the rain. All of the available hotel and motel rooms in the area were booked as emergency housing. I accepted the invitation from a couple at Wesley United Methodist Church to stay with them until my house was repaired. This took about six months before I could move back.

The front page headline ofThe Republican on Friday, June 3, declared "AFTERMATH". The headline on Saturday, June 4, reported "RECOVERY BEGINS". We could not drive onto our street until the city crews had removed and cleaned each street of debris. In my neighborhood, there was major damage on South Main St, Pennsylvania Ave, Beech St, Pine St Court, Central St, opposite from Springfield College campus. Many houses had to demolished and for those owners it took much longer before new housing was built. Many of the families relocated permanently and chose not to return to the neighborhood.

My Retirement Years 2012–2016

One of the traditions at AIC was that faculty who were retiring were invited to present a lecture about their life and work or about a major topic that reflected his or her life. For that event, I wrote a talk which I presented before the faculty and friends. These reflections are adapted and developed from that lecture. In the coming years, I will probably add to it with the goal to tell more about my life and art.

In May 2012, at the age of 65, I retired from teaching at AIC and the Quadrangle. For months I had struggled with being alone. I vacillated between two choices: to remain in the familiar community of colleagues and friends made during the eighteen years in Springfield. Or, to sell my house and move back to Virginia where I had lived from birth until I was forty-seven and the rest of my family had lived for several generations.

Finally, I decided to move back to Alexandria to live in our original family house with my daughter Alyssa. She and I had collaborated at Torpedo in her expanded studio and gallery all of the time I was living in

Massachusetts. By the time of my return to Alexandria in 2012, the Torpedo Factory Art Center had expanded and become world famous. Visitors are welcome to meet some of the one hundred and sixty-five resident artists and watch them work. The variety of art includes ceramics, collage and fixed media, fiber, glass and enamel, jewelry, painting and drawing, photography, printmaking and sculpture. The art center is home to the largest collection of publicly accessible working artist studios in the U.S.

The different media and subjects for our art enabled Alyssa and me to be creative and find new ways to collaborate with each other. I brought with me from Springfield many of my Power Point presentations and academic course notes which could inform our work together. I could also provide resources for her school teaching. I continued my architectural consulting with our family construction business and in creating and selling drawings and prints of area residences, public and private commercial buildings. I am excited about the possibilities of our working together as father and daughter and as professional artists. I anticipate our attendance together at alumnal events at Howard University.

National Museum of African American History and Culture

For many years, with Alyssa or on my own I had enjoyed going into DC to explore the Smithsonian museums and galleries. On September 24, 2016, the National Museum of African American History and Culture opened to the public as the nineteenth and newest museum of the Smithsonian Institution. Because of my involvement with helping to collect many of the artifacts and consult with the architectural staff, she and I had been privileged to visit behind the scene during the pre-opening construction period and observe the progress as the exhibitions were developed. We were confident that we would be returning many more times in the years ahead. This is the only national museum devoted exclusively to the documentation of African American life, history and culture. After decades of efforts to promote and highlight the contributions of African Americans, it was established by Act of Congress in 2003. It is an architectural marvel on a symbolic site, on the National Mall at the center of Washington D.C.'s historic core. Collection donors helped the Museum grow its entire collection of close to 37,000 artifacts and works of art from all over the world.

There are four pillars upon which the NMAAHC stands: It provides an opportunity for those who are interested in African American culture to explore and revel in this history through interactive exhibitions. It helps all Americans see how their stories, their histories, and their cultures are shaped and informed by global influences. It explores what it means to be an American and share how American values like resiliency, optimism, and spirituality are reflected in African American history and culture. Finally, it serves as a place of collaboration that reaches beyond Washington, D.C. to engage new audiences and to work with the myriad of museums and educational institutions that have explored and preserved this important history well before this museum was created. Lonnie G. Bunch III, founding director of the Museum said, "there are few things as powerful and as important as a people, as a nation that is steeped in its history."

Pioneering African American architects, such as Harold L. Williams, Norma Merrick Sklarek and John S. Chase expanded the profession and paved the way for a new generation, including Philip G. Freelon and Michael Marshall. Harold L. Williams (1924-2015) focused on public service for fifty years, primarily in Southern California. His firm, Harold Williams Associated, focused on buildings such as schools, civic centers and city halls. He designed a new Watts Tower Art Center in 1967 to serve the community. He designed Compton City Hall and Civic Center, moving the city and its changing demographics into the future. He helped found the National Organization of Minority Architects (NOMA) in 1971. When Norma Merrick Sklarek (1926-2012) graduated from Columbia University's School of Architecture she was one of the first African American women to receive a license to practice architecture. In 1985, she co-founded Siegel, Sklarek and Diamond with Margot Siegel and Kathrine Diamond, at the time one of the largest women-owned architecture firms in the United States.

The lead designer David Adjaye and lead architect Philip Freelon, together with their architectural team Freelon Adjaye Bond/Smith Group, won an international competition on April 2009 to design and deliver The National Museum of African American History and Culture to the people of the United States. Groundbreaking of the five-acre site took place in February 2012. The son of a Ghanaian diplomat, Adjaye grew up as a citizen of the world, has lived in Egypt, England, Lebanon and Tanzania and has visited all 54 independent nations of Africa. Before his death in 2009, partner J. Max Bond Jr. designed African American historic sites, museums and archives around the world. Philip Freelon was the leading designer for African American museums in America. He designed the Museum of the African Diaspora in San Francisco, the Reginald L. Lewis Museum of Maryland African American History and Culture in Baltimore, the Center for Civil and Human Rights in Atlanta, the Harvey Gantt Center in Charlotte and Emancipation Park in Houston.

The stacked shape of the Museum building was designed by the architects to reflect the stacked top portions of Yoruba carved wood columns by Olowe of Ise found on traditional buildings in Nigeria. The top or corona levels of the exterior of the building are encapsulated or clad by openwork cast aluminum panels. The architects use the word "corona" which is also known as "crown" or "capital".

On the lower level the museum restaurant offered several menus, mostly centering on regional African American cuisine. My favorite so far has been the Creole pan fried catfish Po'boy, yams, green beans and lemon square dessert.

The Museum's Department of Curatorial Affairs focused on scholarship, preservation, and collections to tell the African American story in twelve inaugural exhibitions. The inaugural exhibitions included: A Century in the Making: Building the National Museum of African American History and Culture; Slavery and Freedom; Defending Freedom, Defining Freedom: Era of Segregation 1876-1968; A Changing America: 1968 and Beyond; Power of Place; Making a Way Out of No Way; Double Victory: The African American Military Experience; Musical Crossroads; Visual Art and the American Experience; Taking the Stage; Sports: Leveling the Playing Field. I recommend that every American should make the trip to visit this unique and historic new museum. I look forward to my remaining years and the opportunities to continue creating art and learning about the importance of arts in our lives.

ALEXANDER'S ODYSSEY

SPRINGFIELD | 2016

My name is Alexander Santorini. I am blessed by being given the name of one of the great leaders in ancient Greek history: Alexander the Great from Macedonia. In the middle of the fourth century B.C., King Phillip II of Macedon in northern Greece attacked and captured the weakened Greek city-states. Phillip admired the cultural achievements of the city-states. His dream was to develop a huge Greek army and spread Greek civilization to other lands, including Persia. However, Phillip was assassinated in 336 B.C. before he could realize his dream.

Phillip's son Alexander carried on his father's plans and became one of the greatest soldiers and conquerors in history. He became king at the age of twenty and ruled for only thirteen years, yet created one of the largest empires in the ancient world. Alexander the Great conquered the vast Persian Empire, Egypt, and lands as far east as northern India. The success of his military campaigns was mostly due to his cavalry, a group of about five thousand armed horsemen. A military formation called the phalanx- a solid, moving wall of foot soldiers bearing shields and long spears, also played an important part in his victories. After Alexander died in 323 B.C., at the age of 33, his great empire collapsed. Parts became independent city-states and other parts became independent kingdoms, such as Syria, Egypt and Macedonia. After his death, Macedonia controlled Greece for 200 years.

My Family History

Now let us move from the fourth century B.C., ahead to the twentieth century A.D., with the recent story of my family background. I have been told some history of the Greek immigrants settling in Springfield. The first came in the 1880's and then the number increased at the time of the First World War. The first Greek who settled in Springfield was Eleftherios Pilatas. He became a manager at the Kibbe Candy Factory, which became the employer of many Greeks who came later. Many Greeks worked as bootblacks and shoeshine workers. Many Greek clubs and open café-type restaurants were formed where the men gathered to read the Greek newspapers, drink Greek coffee, discuss politics and exchange ideas.

My paternal and maternal grandparents came to America from Corinth and Athens, Greece, respectively, and arrived in the port of Boston during the 1920's. They came seeking peace and freedom from a time of conflict in Greece. The major public disagreement in Greece was between the premier, who wanted to enter the War on the side of the Allies, and the king and the Royalist party who wanted Greece to stay neutral. After World War I, King Constantine returned to power in 1920 with much public support. The victory of the Allies and the defeat of the Ottoman Turks during the war granted Greece the opportunity to reclaim territory from Turkey. However, the Greeks were bitterly defeated by the Turks in Anatolia in 1922. The king was blamed for this defeat and forced into exile. His son and successor, King George II, reigned until 1924, when Greece became a republic for a short period. Many families never returned to Greece after the war, choosing to wait for lasting peace or to make a fortune in America first. Greece had always been a poor country and the conflict over the war gave many immigrants reason to remain in Springfield.

By 1936, 3,600 Greeks were living in Springfield, scattered mainly within the North End, South End, Forest Park and the Hill neighborhoods. At their peak, Greeks owned and operated over 100 lunch rooms and restaurants throughout the city. At this time, a Greek resident published the **National Union,** described on its masthead as "The only American Hellenic News-Magazine published weekly, Printed in the English language in America."

My father and mother, Theophilus and Persephone Santorini, were married in Boston in 1945 and had two daughters, Alexandra and Penelope, in the next two years, and then moved to Springfield in 1947. My father enlisted in the Army, 102nd Infantry Division, one year before North Korea invaded South Korea in June 1950. His division had started in 1942 and was active in World War II and continued in later years. I was born in 1951 while he was deployed in Korea. My father was killed in action there in February 1952. His body was shipped back for burial in Oak Grove Cemetery in Springfield.

My mother stayed in the house that my parents had bought on Prospect Street, off of Carew Street near Mercy Hospital. Alexandra and Penelope and I lived in this house all of our childhood and youth. My mother's bedroom was furnished with old wooden furniture that my father had brought from Boston. My sisters and I had furniture that had been purchased at the PX at Westover in Chicopee. As a child I remember visiting his grave regularly with my mother and sisters. We sponsored a memorial service for him at St. George's Cathedral each year on the anniversary of his death. Although I recall that most of his anniversary days were brisk and cold, there sometimes would be blue skies and large billowing white and grey cumulus clouds that were signs of hope that spring was on the way.

My mother had saved all of the letters our father had sent her. On special occasions during our childhood, she would share them with us to remember his life and legacy. He described the weather and what he was doing, but always spoke only of the positive activities and not about any hardships or problems. For example, he wrote: "I am doing my part with all of us fighting to protect democracy and our freedoms in America and around the world." Each of his letters ended with variations of this message: "I miss each of you very much. I look forward to the time when I will be back home. My biggest hope is that we soon will be reunited as a family."

One of my father's friends continued as a friend of our family after 1952: Nicholas Sotiropoulos, who had married his wife Christina in 1949 in our cathedral. He was a professional boxer who fought under the name of Nick Stato. He worked as a machinist at American Bosch, where many other Greeks of my parents' and grandparents' generations had worked.

Despite the hardships of being a single parent, our mother managed well, caring for us and taking in work to do at home. She raised Alexandra, Penelope and me by herself until each of us became adults and started our own families. In 1952, working from home, she had started a cooking and catering business. She also prepared and sold food to a delicatessen store.

The Start and Early Years of Santorini Greek Restaurant

In 1956, after my sisters and I were in school full time, my mother Persephone leased a fully-equipped restaurant from another family. She named it the Santorini Greek Restaurant. After several years she was able to buy the entire property. It included a long one-story building with the restaurant space and two other businesses which then continued as tenants paying my mother. A separate adjoining three-story building contained five family apartments and a ground level business tenant. The front ran along the west side of Chestnut Street from the corner of Carew Street. It had two entrances, one from the sidewalk and one from the parking lot behind the building. There were eight booths along the front wall which could seat four people each. There was a long counter with stools which could seat ten customers running parallel to the front row of booths. The waitress could move easily to the booths from behind the counter where the cash register was located. All of the supplies needed by the waitress were on shelves behind the counter. Behind the cash register was an open doorway with a hanging drapery where staff could access the kitchen. The grill and kitchen were behind the wall with a large opening through which the cook received written orders and placed the fulfilled orders back to the waitress. Out of sight beside the kitchen was the food pantry, walk-in freezer and upright cooler. Also behind the kitchen were the deep sinks and dishwasher for washing pots, pans, dishes and utensils. A restroom was accessible at the north end of the dining area at the rear parking lot entrance. For most of the period that she owned it by herself, she did not make any major changes to the layout in the dining area or the kitchen.

This location proved to be a wise decision because it was located where there was regular traffic, within blocks of several apartment buildings, and opposite the Mercy Hospital and the programs of the Sisters of Providence. On diagonal poles mounted on the front of the restaurant, each day when she opened she put up the American flag, Greek flag and **Open** flag, and at the end of the day she took them down.

From the start, she had two printed signs posted on the front door and at the cash register: **Cash Only** and **We Do Not Make Change**.

Our family has never had a license to serve alcoholic beverages. When there were private catered events, our guests could bring their own beverages to consume. This policy encouraged recovering alcoholics, non-drinkers, minors and Muslims to feel welcome during regular business hours. Through all the years of operation, because we were not open after school or on weekends, the majority of our customers were adults. Because we were located in the midst of the wonderful diversity of Springfield our customers came from many different backgrounds, sometimes like a little United Nations.

For the first ten years she served only lunch from 11 am-3 pm, on the weekdays. After my sisters and I were older, she expanded to serve breakfast and lunch from Monday through Friday, 8 am- 3 pm. Once my mother added breakfast to the menu, it was served only from 8 am-11 am, and lunch was served from 11 am-3 pm. The breakfast menu included eggs, bacon, sausage, toast, home fries, omelets, breakfast sandwiches, pancakes and a variety of side dishes, plus Greek desserts. The beverages were the same as provided for lunchtime.

For the luncheon menu, she maintained primarily Greek items because there were not many Greek restaurants still active by that time. She usually did not cook pizza, hamburgers and hot dogs because there were other places that served them regularly. Here are some of the lunch menu items served over the years, either as A la carte individual treats or full meals:

Souvlaki-grilled lamb or beef on a skewer, marinated with tasty seasonings, served with rice pilaf, salad and a roll.

Baked chicken- marinated with lemon and garlic, served with rice pilaf, salad and roll.

Moussaka- a layered casserole of seasoned beef and eggplant with bechamel sauce topping, served with rice pilaf.

Pastitsio- Greek lasagna with bechamel sauce, served with salad.

Gyro Plate-seasoned beef and lamb with tomatoes, onions and *tzatsiki* sauce in a pita pocket; served with rice pilaf and a salad.

Baked fillet of fish prepared with bread crumbs and butter.

Greek seafood platter, such as shrimp, crayfish, lobster, octopus, and squid when available, usually served with a sauce made with lemons and olive oil and the fish is usually fried or grilled.

Lentil soup.

Lamb shank, served with orzo, salad and a roll.

Greek salad, green beans, rice pilaf, *spanakopita* (spinach phyllo pie made of spinach and feta cheese).

Dolmathes -grape leaves stuffed with rice.

There was a variety of Greek desserts, including: *Baklava* (walnut and spice filled phyllo pastry with special syrup); *Diples*- hand wrapped, dipped in honey topped with sesame seeds and nuts; Rice pudding; *Kourambiedes* (butter cookies with powdered sugar); *Finikia* (spiced butter cookies sprinkled with nuts); *Tsoureki*- sweet and butter bread; *Koulourakia* (Greek cookies); *Loukoumades* (hot-puffed deep-fried pastry with honey syrup and cinnamon).

The beverages available were fruit juices, soda, milk, bottled or tap water, tea and Greek or American coffee. Greek coffee is a dark, rich finely ground coffee called *kafe* or *kafedaki*, which is usually brewed in a long-handled pot known as a *briki*. Briki pots come in two-, four-, or six-demitasse sizes. Greek coffee is not made in larger quantities because the foam at the top, which is supposed to bring good luck, will not be of the right consistency. The coffee is served black, moderately sweet, or very sweet, and with a glass of cold water. *Kafedaki* is sipped carefully to avoid disturbing the grounds that settle to the bottom on the cup.

As Alexandra, Penelope and I we became old enough, we helped in the restaurant after the school day and during vacation times. Once we finished high school, we continued working there under our mother's supervision. When each of reached eighteen we became equal partners in ownership with our mother.

St. George Cathedral and Greek Orthodoxy

Since my baptism as an infant, I have been an active member of St. George Greek Orthodox Cathedral. As a child and young person, I learned much about the history, traditions and theology of the Orthodox Church, including the significant history of our faith, the art and architecture of the church sanctuary, and the features of the liturgy. The local Greek Orthodox church was organized in 1907 and its first building was on Auburn Street; the second church building was on Patton Street in 1919.

St. George, the patron saint of the cathedral, lived in the third century. He was born of a Greek father from Cappadocia and a mother from Palestine. He was a military tribune, commander of a thousand troops, and was illustrious in battle. When he learned that the Emperor Diocletian was preparing to persecute the Christians, George presented himself before the Emperor and denounced him. For this act of defiance against the Roman emperor and act of Christian faith, George was tortured and finally beheaded in 296 in Nicomedia. His remains were taken to Lydda, Palestine, the homeland of his mother. Today St. George, the patron saint of shepherds, is one of the most honored and recognized saints in all of Christianity and is also the patron saint of all of Great Britain.

The present cathedral building on Plainfield Street was purchased from the Memorial Congregational Church, which had used the building from 1869 to 1941. The architect was Richard Upjohn who had also designed Trinity Church (Episcopal) on Wall Street in New York City. The estate property had been owned by George Atwater, a wealthy Springfield businessman, on a high rise on Memorial Square overlooking the Connecticut River. Patterned after the famous Tiffany stained glass window designs, the New York Stained Glass Window Company created the windows in the sanctuary. One of the windows on the eastern side depicts a view of George Atwater's property, Rockrimmon Estate. A wealthy quarry owner in Monson donated all the granite for the edifice.

After the Orthodox Church bought the property from the Congregational church in 1941 it was transformed with Orthodox features and decorations and reconsecrated as the new cathedral. The organ and choir seats originally were in the front of the sanctuary, but they were relocated to the balcony at the back. Traditionally the altar area is located at the eastern end of the sanctuary, but St. George's altar is at the north end of the building. The beautiful *iconostasis* or icon screen was built to separate the altar area from the rest of the sanctuary. The Gothic architecture of St. George's does not have the traditional domed ceiling, representing the expanse of heaven. However, the idea of the church as a place where heaven and earth meet is expressed in the soaring lines of the building, and the icons of the saints and apostles who look upon the worshippers from above. The Beautiful Gate in front of the altar is only used by the priest during worship services. To the right of this gate is the icon of Christ, the Light- giver; to the left is the icon of Christ with the Virgin Mary, showing how the Son became fully human, taking humanity from the Virgin.

To the right of the iconostasis is the *cathedra*, or the chair for the bishop of the cathedral. Behind the chair is an icon of Christ as Pantocrator. Around the front of the pulpit are icons of the four Gospel writers and Christ with the orb, representing the world. At the back of the sanctuary, with the red votive glasses and long white candles in the sand, there are three icons: St. George slaying the dragon, Christ blessing, and the Virgin Mary with the Christ child.

✝ ✝ ✝

To broaden our understanding here is some information about the history of the Greek Orthodox church. From the death of Jesus in 33 AD there was one unified Christian Church until the Eastern Schism. The separation of the Eastern Church, with its headquarters at Constantinople, and the Western Church centered in Rome, cannot be assigned a precise date because it was not a single event but rather the result of an increasing estrangement that culminated with the vengeful destruction of the Byzantine Empire by the crusaders of the Latin Empire. The pope excommunicated the patriarch, causing the Great Schism which became a permanent split. In recent years the pope rescinded the excommunication and the pope and patriarch have maintained positive dialogue.

There are now thousands of different denominations or traditions. Since the Eastern Schism, which divided the Western and Eastern Church, the Orthodox Church continues to assert that it is the earliest tradition. The Roman pope appointed Charlemagne to strengthen the Western Church which led to many heresies and divided councils over the time of many popes and emperors.

St. Basil's Day, which falls on New Year's Day, celebrates the patron saint of the poor and needy. Gifts are exchanged and special St. Basil's Cake is served. Epiphany, on January 6, marks the end of the Christmas season. In seaside villages in Greece and Greek communities in the diaspora, the Blessing of the Waters takes place. The event is of great importance to Greek sailors, whose vessels had been idle during the twelve days from Christmas to Epiphany.

The Orthodox call the holy day celebrating the resurrection of Jesus Christ *Pascha*, based on the Passover. They do not use the term "Easter" which was a pagan name for the Spring festival. *Pascha* is the most important holiday in the calendar of the Greek Orthodox Church and is celebrated according to the Julian calendar. The Orthodox Liturgy which is followed every Sunday through the year is almost exactly the same as was used in the 3rd century.

One of the primary values among Greek families is *philotimo*, a word that describes the feeling of honor that is part of the daily behavior of many Greeks. *Philotimo* involves gaining the respect of others for oneself and one's family by upholding the family honor. It is important at all levels of society and is a value passed on from generation to generation. Our Santorini family honor was also associated with service to the United States of America and its values. Generations of our family who had not come to America had a similar appreciation of the family honor of serving Greece and its national values.

My father's Army division, the 102nd Infantry, had disbanded in 1965, but I entered another unit to provide support for the men and women serving in the Vietnam Conflict. In January 1966, as a single man I entered the Army, as a cook. The bombing of Hanoi area of North Vietnam by U.S. planes had begun June 29. Within the next six months there were 385,000 US troops stationed in South Vietnam. I was one of them. In the "Tet Offensive", Communist troops attacked several provincial capitals and other major cities, including Saigon, on Jan 30, 1968.

Peace talks began in Paris in 1968 and all bombing of the north stopped October 31. On April 4 Dr. Martin Luther King, Jr was assassinated in Memphis, Tennessee. Robert F. Kennedy was shot and killed June 5 in Los Angeles. In 1969 the four-party Vietnam peace talks began. The highest peak of US troops in Vietnam reached 543,400 in April 1969 and the withdrawal of our troops began July 8, 1969. During my time in the Army and Vietnam, back in Springfield my mother, her sisters and my sisters managed all of the restaurant responsibilities, although they decreased the hours to 11 am- 3 pm.

My spirits were always lifted when I received a letter from my mother or one of my sisters. And I was pleased each time I received a letter from Athena, one of the young women I had known in our church youth group. She, her mother, father and her brother had moved from Boston to Springfield when Athena was in high school. In late 1969, I was discharged honorably and returned home to civilian life. I began dating Athena and after a year back in Springfield, we became engaged.

My marriage to Athena

Athena and I were married in St. George Cathedral in 1972. I was so happy and proud to be marrying her in the church in which I had been raised and she had joined in her high school years. After she walked down the central aisle the music of Johann Pachelbel's "Canon", escorted by her father, we stood side by side and took part in the betrothal ceremony. Athena, who always looked beautiful to me all the time, was especially shining, with her long black hair tied back in a bun. Her bright white gown of silk brocade, hand-embroidered train and headpiece were all stunning. I was wearing a black tuxedo with cummerbund and bowtie matching the pastel blue of her bridal party. My full head of curly black hair and bushy moustache were recently trimmed. Both of us were grinning broadly throughout the ceremony.

The priest placed a lighted candle in each of our right hands, symbolizing the perpetual light of Christ and the light of virtue and unity in our lives. The one candle on the table represented the union of two in one. Father then blessed both rings. Taking the groom's ring he declared that I was betrothed to Athena; he repeated this ritual three times. Next, he performed the same ritual with Athena's ring three times and declared that she was betrothed to me.

Then Athena's mother stood before us and interchanged the rings three times, in the name of the Holy Trinity, signifying that we would mutually look after each other's welfare. We received the rings and joined our right hands together. Her mother, as the *koumbara*, blessed the rings. Her brother, as the *kuombaro*, placed the crowns on our heads and exchanged the crowns three times on each of our heads. The white ribbon that connected the two crowns indicated that God blessed and exalted us in our relationship to one another. Following the reading from the scriptures, Athena and I sipped three times from the common cup, representing the cup of life. We promised to share in all the joys and sorrows, happiness and sadness together. The crowning sealed and consummated the marriage as God joined us in a mystical and holy union. Next, we completed the ceremonial walk around the table three times, led by the priest chanting hymns of joy. This ceremony symbolized that Christ would lead us in our journey throughout life and would guide our lives by His Word. The ceremony concluded with the benediction.

A few months before our marriage Athena and I had bought a house on Bartlett Street, off Carew Street. It was a triple decker building with a porch on each level overlooking the street. With two separate entrances, we shared the house with another family. My mother and my sister Alexandra and her new husband continued to live in my mother's house on Prospect Street around the corner. My sister Penelope and her husband bought their own house, on Massasoit Street, parallel to Bartlett Street and connected to Prospect Street. Although our houses were not on the same street, we were in the same residential neighborhood, and only a few blocks from our family restaurant.

After our wedding, my sisters, their spouses, Athena and I took over the shared management and equal ownership of Santorini Greek Restaurant, which we had continued at the same location on the corner of Chestnut Street and Carew Street. As the years progressed all of us cross-trained for all of the responsibilities of the restaurant so that we could easily cover for each other smoothly.

In 1974, Athena and I had our first child, Michael. While Athena cared for him at home and helped when possible at the business, I worked as the cook alongside Alexandra and Penelope and two more workers. Our restaurant continued the days and hours started by our mother: open Monday through Friday for breakfast and lunch, but closed every Saturday and Sunday in order to allow our family to have two days of rest from our work. This schedule also enabled our families to participate in most of the services and activities at St. George's and still maintain our business. Over the years we owned several different vans to transport food from our vendors to the restaurant, or to our off-site catering events. The two vehicles that lasted the longest were a Chevy Express with cold AC and containing a cage, racks and bins and a Ford Transit 250 Cargo van.

Hospitality, or *philoxenia,* is an old Greek tradition. Some people believe that the harshness of the Greek landscape many have caused Greeks to be kind to anyone in need of food or shelter. It is a value shared by many other Mediterranean nations. It is also central to the teaching of the Greek Orthodox Church. Hospitality has always been a major value of our family and our restaurant. A beautiful large mural depicting the Greek island of Santorini filled one entire wall, representing our ancestral Greek island home and our family name. The words "Hospitality" and "*Philoxenia*" were prominent on another wall, welcoming all who come for food, drink and fellowship. Another sign that greeted our customers was "*Kali Orexi*" with the translation beside it: "Good appetite."

Our restaurant was regularly visited by people of all backgrounds, representing the diversity of our Springfield neighborhood. Regularly we played background recorded music of songs from several different cultures and relating to our customers' identities. Many of the older Greek folk songs that we played were in the eastern style with keys or modes known as *dhimotika* or *makamia*. Much of the dance music of the groups or *koumpania* in mainland Greece are still played in this modal way. The eastern or Oriental flavor is most evident in rembetika and amanadhes, most prominent in the first half of the 20th century and revived in the 1970s. Greek folk music from the music cafes in Izmir and Istanbul. Groups played a style known as *café amanes* or *amanadaes,* after the refrain "*Aman, Aman*" or "Mercy, mercy." *Rembetika* had always been the music of the poor and dispossessed, and combined with the musical style of the eastern Mediterranean with lyrics telling of the plight and joys of the lower class folk. At times when many of our customers were Irish, Italian or Hispanic, we would play background music from their traditions. During holidays and holiday seasons, we would play popular holiday music. This pleased our guests and also showed our respect for the different groups from our neighborhood.

We never had a TV in the restaurant because we wanted to encourage our customers to visit with each other. In the early days of the business, most of our customers were Greek, but as the years progressed and the neighborhood became more varied we served people of every possible origin. Especially, we welcomed new immigrants and celebrated the freedom and heritage of our American and Springfield society. We encouraged courtesy and respect for all people. On one wall we had a poster of the **Bill of Rights of the U.S. Constitution.** Near it was a sign with the Greek alphabet and each letter's phonetic spelling, so that people could learn the source of the English alphabet from the original Greek.

The death of our mother Persephone and the funeral service

Due to her weakening health and congestive heart failure for a few years, my mother, Persephone Santorini, spent less time in the restaurant and more time at her home with Alexandra and her family. She died of a heart attack at home in June 1984. All of my close-knit family had been aware of her failing health but her actual death was difficult for each of us, especially for my sisters. The basic parts of the Orthodox funeral service can be traced mainly to the fifth century and with the passage of centuries, the liturgy has been enriched with psalms and hymns to become one of the most versatile and moving services of the Orthodox tradition. By the time of my mother's death, I had participated in many funeral services. The purposes of the service were to help us develop a more profound understanding of the meaning of life, to help us deal with the emotions at the time of death. The service also emphasized that death for the Christian is not the end, and affirmed our hope in salvation and eternal life, and recognized the existence and expression of the emotions of grief.

The service emphasized the reality of human existence, the frailty of life and the vanity of worldly things. It directed our minds to reflect on the value of the eternal blessings of God. I found while listening to the liturgy for my mother that it was a sacred time to meditate on my own relationship with God and the orientation of my life. I also could pray fervently for the forgiveness and repose of my mother who had been transferred to the life beyond the grave. Central to this liturgy was the *Trisagion* or "Thrice-Holy" service which is chanted on the evening before the service, on the day of the service, at the graveside, and for subsequent memorial services. This service was so named because it began with the familiar prayer, "Holy God, Holy Mighty, Holy Immortal, have mercy on us," repeated three times. After the initial prayers, four hymns were chanted asking the Lord to give rest to the deceased. A litany followed and concluded with a prayer that included the petition to the Lord to grant rest to the deceased and asked for forgiveness of sins. Before the service was concluded, the faithful sang, "May your memory be eternal."

Then three stanzas of verses from Psalm 119 were chanted beginning with the words: "Blessed are those whose way is blameless, who walk in the law of the Lord." Following the chanting of Psalm 119 were the Funeral Praises, the *Evlogetaria*, meaning "hymns of praise." Each hymn was proceeded by Psalm 119:12: "Blessed are You, O Lord, teach me your statutes." At the conclusion of the *Evlogetaria*, the *Kontakion* of the service was chanted: "With the Saints give rest, O Christ, to the soul of Your servant where there is no pain, nor sorrow, nor suffering, but life everlasting." During the chanting of this hymn, the priest censed the deceased and the faithful, as well as the Holy Altar Table and icons. Following this were the hymns known as the *Idiomela*. Each hymn had its own particular melody and were sung in the order of the eight modes or tones of Byzantine chant. The funeral service also included two Scripture lessons, one from the *Apostolos* (the liturgical book that contains the lections from the Book of Acts and the Epistles) and another from the *Evangelion* (the liturgical book of the four Gospels arranged in pericopes or lections). The assigned readings for the service were I Thessalonians 4:13-17 and John 5: 24-30.

Following the readings, the priest offered a prayer for the repose of the deceased. The Dismissal prayer of the service introduced the hope of the resurrection. Following the Dismissal prayer, the people came forward to look upon the deceased, and to offer a kiss to the deceased, an expression of love for the departed and an affirmation that the one who has fallen asleep is worthy of the fulfillment of God's promises.

After the church service we rode behind the hearse holding her casket to Oak Grove Cemetery. There the casket was interred in the space next to my father's grave. The priest chanted again the *Trisagion* at the cemetery. Our family plot was close to the Tapley Street entrance into the cemetery near the corner of St. George East Avenue and Border Avenue. Tall pine trees and large old oak trees were dominant in this area. On this day there was a clear blue sky with slow moving soft cumulus clouds moving along the horizon.

Many of the members of families of our faith community were buried in this same section, some of whom are listed here alphabetically: Andros, Anamisis, Hamilakis, Kastrinakis, Kirastoulis, Kontekakis Millasos, Poules, Sotiropoulos, Stathis, Symiakakis, Trikounakis, Vlastos, Zeimbekakis. Stopping at each of their graves brought back many beloved memories of those I had known. Including all the others buried in the cemetery, they were all "saints of God". When I returned to our family plot throughout the years, I would often stop and pray at many of these graves. We were surrounded by "a great cloud of witnesses who have gone before us."

The annual Glendi Festival

In 1977 the Greek Cultural Center was developed from the former Memorial Square Library across the street from the Cathedral to provide more space for the growing needs of the parish, and the first Glendi festival began in 1978. Starting in the same year, my mother, sisters and I had volunteered to prepare and serve the food, along with many other parish volunteers. Let me describe some of the highlights of the three-day Glendi Festival held each year in September. Welcoming the many guests inside our cultural center were our pastor and his wife. After my mother's death, my wife Athena, son Michael and I continued our family involvement at the festival. Every weekend of the festival for thirty-eight years, to 2016, Athena and I worked at the festival and encouraged our restaurant patrons and the community to attend.

The Festival foods provided many of the same items served in our restaurant, mainly because we were in charge of much of the Festival food service, working with a large crew of church volunteers. Many other parish families and members provided certain foods that were their particular specialties. Here are the foods that the men, women and youth of our parish provided during the festival, including al a carte individual treats or full meals. *Souvlaki*, baked chicken, *Moussaka*, *Pastitsio*, *Gyro*, Baked fillet of fish, lentil soup, lamb shank, Greek salad, rice pilaf, *spanakopita*, and *Dolmathes*. There was a variety of Greek desserts, including: *Baklava*, *Diples*, rice pudding, *kourambiedes*, *finikia Tsoureki*, *Kouloura-kia and Loukoumades*. The beverages available were beer, wine, ouzo, soda, bottled water and coffee (Greek and American).

In addition to all the food, the festival also featured live Greek music provided by Hellenic Express and Greek folk dancing performed in the outdoor amphitheatre by the Glendi Dancers and the Cretan Dancers wearing traditional Greek costumes. I took part in folk dancing at family and church ceremonies, whether solemn or festive, starting as a child and then all the way through my youth and into my adult years. Athena and Michael also learned folk dancing. Michael participated with our church dancers through all his school years, advancing into different groups based on age. At the festival, because both Athena and I were involved in preparing and serving the food, we rarely had time or energy to take part in much of the dancing. But, holding hands, we would usually sit and watch, and cheer on the dancers. In the evening, anyone could join in the dancing, from the youngest toddlers to the eldest men and women. Greek folk dances are usually performed by a group of people, either arm in arm in a line, or in an open circle moving counterclockwise. The leader of the group often improvised, while the others followed the basic steps.

There are four traditional folk dances that are included each year in the Glendi Festival. The *syrtaki*, a mellow and expressive dance, is the most famous Greek dance. The *hasapiko*, or butcher's dance, includes several men dancing slowly, holding each other's hands, and doing the same steps in a solemn style. The *tsamiko* is also called the handkerchief dance because the leader and the next dancer hold onto a handkerchief. The leader performs acrobatic stunts, using the handkerchief for support while the second dancer is holding it. This dance was widely performed by freedom fighters in the war for independence. The *kalamatiano* is the national dance of Greece. It is a happy, festive dance that originated in the Peloponnese but is now performed throughout the country. *Kalamatiano* dancers stand in a row with their hands on each other's shoulders.

Alongside the American flag, the Greek national flag waved from the flag pole at the amphitheatre. The Greek flag consists of nine horizontal blue and white stripes with a white cross in the upper left corner. Blue and white represent the sea and the mountains of Greece. The cross symbolizes the Greek Orthodox Church.

A traditional pastime for Greek men in a *kafeneio* (restaurant) is to click away at their worry beads. The beads are strung on thread and held in the hand. The clicking sounds that is made as the fingers count the beads creates a type of background music that accompanies lively conversations. Greek men have been using worry beads for centuries, although their beads or *komboloi*, have little to do with worry. It is suggested that the use of these beads is one of the oldest and simplest ways to relieve stress. They have been first used in India by Hindus and Buddhists as prayer beads, and later adopted by the Muslims. The Greeks may have adopted their use from the Turks, who are Muslim. The use of these beads in Greece never achieved any religious significance, but rather became a secular pastime practiced by older men.

During the Glendi Festival, in the gymnasium and lower level there were treasures, religious items and vendors. Outside in our parking lot and under the large tent there were more food items for sale: hot dogs, hamburgers, Loukoumathes, Gyros, beer and wine. Visitors could tour and learn about our Byzantine Chapel and the Cathedral across Plainfield Street.

Our son Michael

Two years after the birth of Michael, in 1976, Athena developed symptoms of bloating, stomach pain, and weakness. After many tests her gynecologist diagnosed that she had ovarian cancer. She had a hysterectomy and had some chemotherapy which completely removed the cancer. However, she would no longer be able to become pregnant and have additional children. With sadness and difficulty Athena and I accepted that Michael would be our only child. She was a loving and devoted mother to Michael and a loving aunt to the children of Alexandra and Penelope, our nieces and nephews. Throughout Michael's childhood and youth, our lives revolved around our family, the restaurant and the church.

As a family, Athena, Michael and I often would visit the Springfield Library and Museums. One of our favorite museums there was the George Walter Vincent Smith Art Museum, especially its gallery of Classical casts, sculpture from Ancient and Renaissance masterpieces. The plaster casts based on original works in Greece and Italy were created and collected in order to allow museum visitors and art students to appreciate the beautiful art works without having to travel to Europe. Michael based several of his history, literature and art class projects in high school on some of the classical works that he had visited in the Museum.

Many Greek sculptures are now lost and known only through the marble and bronze copies made primarily in the 1st century B.C. by the Romans. The plaster copies are made from those Roman reproductions. The process of copying was facilitated for the Romans by the use of plaster molds taken from the original Greek sculptures. These molds were then distributed to copyists' workshops throughout the Roman Empire and used to make plaster casts the same size as the originals.

Here are some of his favorite ancient Greek works in the Springfield cast gallery. Dione and Aphrodite, 438-432 B.C., Greek Classical from the workshop of Phidias, from the south side of the east pediment of the Parthenon. Eleusinian Relief of Demeter, Persephone and Triptolemus, based on a marble relief carved in 440 B.C., in early Classical Greece and found in Eleusis in 1859. Frieze, c. 447-432 B.C., from the workshop of Phidias, Greek Classical, scenes from the frieze on the Parthenon. Hermes carrying the infant Dionysus, c. 343 B.C., from the Temple of Hera at Olympia. Ionic Capital, c. 421-405 B.C., Greek Classical from a capital on the Erechtheum, Acropolis, Athens. Laocoon Group, the ancient Hellenistic group of the dying Laocoon and his two sons carved from marble by Agesander, Athenodorus and Polydorus of Rhodes probably in the early 1st century B.C. Nike loosening sandal, 410-407 B.C., by Agorakritos, Greek Classical, from the balustrade surrounding the Temple of Athena Nike, Acropolis, Athens. Relief of Athena, Victory, GE, 180 B.C., Greek Hellenistic, from the east side of the Altar of Zeus, Pergamon. Sophocles, c.340-330 B.C., probably late Greek Classical, from the north side of the east pediment of the Parthenon. Venus of Melos, Late Greek Hellenistic, 150-120 B.C., from a sanctuary on the island of Melos.

In 1988, Athena, Michael and I went on a summer vacation to Greece and the Islands while Michael was in high school. Organized with a group from our parish, the trip included a bus land tour of Athens, Corinth, Delphi and a cruise ship tour to Crete, Rhodes, Delos, Mykonos and Santorini. None of our extended family still lived in Greece, but had all settled in America. There were political and economic problems in the country and conflict with several of the adjoining nations over many decades. In most recent years, the extreme national debt crisis also meant that the opportunities for tourists were almost completely decimated. We preferred to recall the ancient Golden Age of Greece or to look forward to a time when modern Greece again will be able to welcome international visitors.

Santorini was the island where our family ancestors had lived but had moved to the mainland for better jobs and housing. The island was named in the thirteenth century, and is a contraction of *Santa Irini* or Saint Irene. Before that it was known as Thera, in the classic Greek, and is still known officially by that name. It is the largest island of a small, circular archipelago, the remnant of a volcanic caldera. The island was the site of one of the largest volcanic eruptions in recorded history: the Minoan eruption which occurred about 3,600 years ago at the height of the Minoan civilization. The eruption may had led indirectly to the collapse of the Minoan civilization on the island of Crete, 61 miles to the south, through a gigantic tsunami. The island is the result of repeated sequences of shield volcano construction followed by caldera collapse. The inner coast around the caldera is a sheer precipice of more than a 980 feet drop at its highest. This coast exhibits the various layers of solidified lava on top of each other, with the main town perched along the crest.

Visiting the Acropolis in Athens was another of the highlights of our trip. The ancient Great Panathenaic Festival played an important part in the history of the Parthenon, figures in its sculptural decorations and the occasion of its dedication. The celebration in 490 B.C., took place several weeks before the Athenians defeated the Persians on the plain of Marathon. The festival of 478 B.C., after the destruction of Athens by the Persians, took place ultimately triumphant. By 450 B.C., the barbarians had been expelled from all Greek lands. Athens turned its attention and resources to the rebuilding of the city and the conception of a new temple for Athena, the goddess of the city itself, which would honor both Athena and the city. In 442 B.C., the workshops and masons' yards were busy with the actual creation of the new temple and the carving of sculptures which would present the Classical ideal of the human and the divine. The annual celebration in 438 B.C., celebrated the completion and dedication of the Parthenon. The symbolism and narrative of the great sculptures of the Parthenon illustrated the role of Athens at Marathon with the defeat of the Persians and the conduct and purpose of the Great Panathenic Festival.

Santorini Greek Restaurant

Michael enjoyed all of his school courses and was a devoted student, especially in his culinary classes. He wanted to work in the restaurant as much as possible, so that he could be prepared to work full time with me after high school graduation. He enjoyed watching college and professional sports on TV. Since the restaurant hours corresponded with the time he was in school, he worked with me mostly after the restaurant was closed in the later afternoon and evenings, during school vacations and with private catered events. He graduated from high school in 1992 and that summer began working full time with me. Often he and I would attend weekend regional cooking and restaurant trade shows. For the next ten years Michael and I worked side-by-side working in the restaurant. It was a special joy for Athena and me to have this time with our son as he worked with us. My sisters Penelope and Alexandra, their husbands and their children also were regular workers with us, as we shared in all the responsibilities of owning and managing the Santorini Greek Restaurant.

Here is a sketch of some of the customers on a typical day in the restaurant. Throughout the seasons, our restaurant provided a comfortable warm atmosphere on cold days or a cool interior on hot days. This was the scene on one hot July day. A short red haired woman in her sixties wearing a bright red shirt and black pants reading the **Springfield Republican** while her husband in a red shirt and black pants matching hers was checking his iPhone after placing their breakfast order. A 14-year-old boy with a Mohawk haircut, father with a Red Sox cap and the mother with her black hair peeking out from behind her hijab, enjoying their lunch. Three teenagers drinking soda and laughing with each other: one with a large Afro, wearing a grey sweatshirt and an Old Navy bag in his hands; the second wearing a neon green T-shirt, brown camo pants and Nike sneakers; the third in a green jacket with a hoodie, loose blue pants and bright red sneakers. Another couple at the counter: a thin African American man in dark brown T-shirt, grey sweatpants and a Yankees cap; his wife in a motorized wheel chair, black hair with bangs, sunglasses on her forehead, red blouse top with bare arms, blue denim jeans and a black leather watch. In a booth an Hispanic mother in a white top, tight black pants and brown hair in bun on top; father with a thin mustache, dark glasses, blue denim jeans, and US Army cap; their toddler in a stroller. My sister sweeping the floor, clearing a table, spraying and wiping table surfaces after each customer left.

As a cook I was motivated by Anthony Bourdain who emphasized that he began his career as a cook and still respected the work of cooks. He was one of the best food journalists in the world. He was straightforward and honest on TV and in person, good use of language and a great storyteller. His autobiographical book **Kitchen Confidential** was a big success about the cooking and restaurant industry. People all over the world had read his books or watched his popular programs such as **No Reservations**, or **Parts Unknown**. As a cook, his life and programs had been influential on me as he combined excellent TV journalism with learning about the foods of different countries and learning about the daily life and culture of the country. His interviews and conversations with people centered on their family meals or meals at restaurants was always enlightening. Anthony Bourdain influenced me to observe and follow his curious spirit, honesty, leaning about food and culture. He once said, "with an open mouth, heart, eyes and mind you can eat anything." He also said "If you don't accept the food, you are rejecting the people. I try to be a good guest." He was genuinely interested in everyone he met.

Many times just before or after closing I met for lunch with Roger, one of our regular Catholic customers and neighbors. Out of mutual respect and interest, we discussed the common and divided history and practices of Eastern Orthodoxy and Roman Catholicism. We also discussed the cultural differences and close connections between ancient Greek and Roman civilizations. Although our two cultures were located geographically next to each other, major differences and conflicts in political and religious history have divided us. More recently, dialogue or bilateral talks have been established between the two faith traditions at the international level. We often discussed the question: How does this translate into our ecumenical relations at the local level? We developed our personal spiritual ecumenism, praying for each other, listening to each other, visiting each other's churches and sharing experiences. The two of us have enjoyed and valued our own dialogues and have come to appreciate our two faith traditions.

On special evening occasions, when our extended family wanted to celebrate a family event, but did not want to be busy preparing and cooking the food, we often dined at Nadim's Mediterranean Grill on Main Street, in downtown Springfield. Nadim's was open in the evening until 11 pm. Some of my favorite menu items were lentil soup, any form of chicken, beef or lamb. I also loved their Mediterranean pasta, especially spaghetti, with kalamata olives, tomatoes, artichokes and feta cheese.

Our son Michael's death

In early 2001, Michael enlisted in the Army, Infantry Division and was away training for much of that year. On September 11, 2001, two highjacked commercial airliners struck the World Trade Center in New York City. The third hijacked plane crashed into the Pentagon and the fourth airliner crashed in Shanksville, PA. 3,000 people were killed in these attacks, the worst terrorist attack on American soil in history. Within a few weeks US and British planes attacked Afghan-based terrorist organization Al-Queda and the Afghanistan's ruling Taliban militia. In response to 9/11, by March 2002, Michael was one of the 1,200 US troops deployed in Afghanistan in Operation Anaconda.

Our son was killed in action near Kabul in October 2002. His body was returned to Bradley International Airport and then driven in the hearse to the funeral home. The Army honor guard and our family welcomed the casket as it was removed from the plane. Three days later, the priest of St. George's Cathedral officiated at the funeral liturgy in our cathedral. Although the Massachusetts Veterans Memorial Cemetery in Agawam had first opened in May 2001, we decided to keep our deceased family members, veterans and civilians, together in our family plot in Oak Grove cemetery.

The liturgy was the same as that followed for my mother's funeral service in 1984. Most meaningful to Athena and me at Michael's service was the *Trisagion* which began with the familiar prayer, "Holy God, Holy Mighty, Holy Immortal, have mercy on us," repeated three times. The four hymns were chanted asking the Lord to give rest to the deceased, followed by the litany and the petition prayer to grant rest to the deceased and for the forgiveness of their sins. Before the service was concluded, the faithful sang, "May your memory be eternal."

Athena and I felt comfort in our grief as we listened to the chants: "Blessed are those whose way is blameless, who walk in the law of the Lord." We received further comfort with the chanted words: "With the Saints give rest, O Christ, to the soul of Your servant where there is no pain, nor sorrow, nor suffering, but life everlasting." The hymns known as the *Idiomela*, which were sung in the order of the eight modes or tones of Byzantine chant were beautiful and moving. Also helpful especially in the days ahead were reading of I Thessalonians 4:13-17 and John 5: 24-30.

After the service and the interment in the cemetery, including the ceremony of giving us the American flag which had draped his casket after we left the church, we returned to the Greek Cultural center. The men and women of our church prepared and served the reception. The gathering of many of Michael's friends and our friends and family provided the love and comfort which we needed so deeply.

Athena and I were grief-stricken at the death of our son, our only child. The only solace was that we knew he had found great purpose and meaning in fighting against the force of terrorism, what had become known as the Global War on Terrorism. In the days ahead our church friends and many of our customers surrounded us with their love and support. We were not alone and our faith in God gave us comfort. But nothing could fill the void made by his death.

In the years ahead, as a veteran myself and as Gold Star parents we took part in many of the Veterans and Memorial Day observances and other events in the Springfield area. We developed many friendships with those who shared the mutual and common loss. We are ever grateful for these relationships and activities. Every Friday of each Memorial Day weekend we attended the observance of laying the wreathes in front of the monuments along the Veterans Way opposite the Symphony Hall. All of the veterans who served in World War I, World War II, Korea and Vietnam are remembered. The row of memorial monuments is, to me, a sacred and honored space to recall all those who have died in many different wars. The fact that across the street stand the Symphony Hall and the City Hall, both in the style of the classical Greek temples and public buildings, brought together both our Greek heritage and our love and service to civic and national duty. The place was personally meaningful to me as a place to remember both my father, my son and all those who had given their lives in service to the ideals of our American democracy, based on its creation by the ancient Greeks.

I have lost several of my friends in the military, by suicide, alcoholism or drug addiction, and accidents. Many times over the years I have had to call the police and ambulance when I arrived at work and found a person unconscious behind my restaurant or at the front door.

Athena became more active in Philoptothos, the women's charitable group at St George's, and shared in other activities at church with me. Almost every Sunday we attended the liturgy together, celebrating our love for each other and our love for our God and church. For the next eight years, we followed a regular routine in working together at the restaurant and sharing most of our free time together. We spent lots of time with her family and my family, who by now were all one big family. Every holiday was an opportunity for food and fellowship as each of us aged in different ways, sometimes following different interests but bound together by blood, the church and our family business.

My wife Athena's dementia and living at home

In 2010 Athena began to show symptoms of dementia with changes in memory, thinking and reasoning. She was diagnosed with being in the early stage of Alzheimer's Disease. I began to notice changes in her behavior, such as coming up with the right name or word, trouble remembering names when introduced to new people, challenges performing familiar tasks, forgetting material that she had just read, getting lost in familiar places, and increasing trouble with planning or organizing. For two years, I cared for her at home as long as I was able. I kept my daily work routine and then maintained a daily routine at home that helped her know the sameness of each day. The hardest part of her illness watching her gradually forgot about Michael and our other family members and friends. Although I regularly burned a candle to remember Michael at home and at church, she was no longer able to remember him or all of our shared memories as a family. Memory can be both a curse and a blessing. She no longer had the pain and suffering of the loss so that was a blessing, but she also could not remember all that I could still recall, and that was a curse. I had lost a son; now I was losing the personality and characteristics of my beloved wife, even though she was still physically alive.

At home, we had two parakeets in a cage, and a cat which had free range of the house, all of which were taken care of by my wife. One of the early signs of her dementia was her neglecting to do the routine tasks to take care of the birds and the cat, such as feeding, cleaning the cage or the litter box. Or she would repeat some tasks more often during the day because she forgot that she had already done them. I was responsible to take care of Fetch, our golden retriever. He loved the twice daily walks outside and runs at the park. He especially loved the snow and winter but was most excited, chasing any objects I threw out for him to bring back, or other objects he would discover and bring for me to throw. Of course, this was all compounded because I was always calling him by name, and he always was fetching something. I guess if I had named him Stay, he would always be by my side

Athena used to prepare the foods with other women and girls for Glendi, but would now forget how to prepare recipes that she had been doing for years. Increasingly I would spend the time with the men and boys in other parts of preparing and serving the food for the festival. Among the early signs of dementia, she would forget the name of a person or would repeat the same story soon after first telling it. She forgot the names of the teacher of her classes or the classmate who was her best friend. Sometimes the name of a person would come back. I'd joke with her and say, "don't wake me up at three in the morning to tell me you remembered Judith's name. Save it for the morning. "As years went on, it became not just a funny incident, but would be embarrassing." When her two parakeets and my dog died, I decided not to replace them with new pets since I had been overwhelmed with taking care of them plus Athena. Soon she didn't even remember her parakeets at all. The cat was still living and stayed inside. Although she no longer remembered the cat's name, she did enjoy having it curl up on her lap where she could pet it.

I would regularly practice some tips to help her or me to remember names or events. Before going to an event together, we would practice the names of those who would also be there. I would Imagine the face of the person and repeat the name several times. When we arrived, it became easier to recall since we had practiced. But as time went on, Athena was unable to remember even with advance practice, although I could. I eventually stopped trying and began to accept the progress of her disease.

Sometimes I would have "a senior moment" or "a brain freeze". The little lapses would concern me as I wondered if they were the early signs of dementia, or Alzheimer's. The primary complaint among my senior friends is forgetting a name or a common word. Before a school reunion, looking at class yearbook, connecting memories and faces before attending was helpful. But I learned that these little lapses occur in most people, and that they do increase as one grows older. I learned that occasional forgetfulness is expected and ordinary, and is not necessarily a sign of developing Alzheimer's.

I learned that remembering is a process that is very quick in our brain. The process: eyes communicate with the visual processing center of the brain. That information moves to the region responsible for recognition of faces. Then to the main memory processing center, seeking out associations. Then moves to the language area of the brain which locate the sounds that form the name of the person. Then that information goes to the speech area and the mouth. All of these regions: occipital lobe, fusiform gyrus, hippocampus and the temporal gyrus are in different locations in the brain. The connections occur within a millisecond. This is especially true about names which are abstract constructions.

I learned that doing word games helps delay the normal situations of forgetfulness: crossword puzzles, anagrams, word quizzes. The cognitive slowdown is the result of the white matter degrading as one grows older. Going to a room and forgetting why we went there; the simple advice is to repeat the steps, think of what is in the room, what we were doing before. Forgetfulness is a sign of aging, like insomnia or weaker muscles or knees. These lapses are momentary and there are ways to help overcome them. I often make a list of where I am planning to go and then and drive in the order of the tasks. Personally, I learned how to recall a name or word that I could not recall. I would go through the alphabet or think of sounds connected with the word. I would picture an image of several things, like call John go to the dentist and pickup milk, I would picture John at the dentist with milk. I would relax when trying to recall, rather than stress about it. I would think of an acronym, if I had a short list of things to buy at the store. Or I would make a list of groceries or items to buy. I often would keep the list in my head and have them remembered by first letters, such as "pbjmbfv": peanut butter, jelly, milk, bread, fruit, vegetable.

After the two years of taking care of Athena in our home, it became clear that she was needing constant attention and that her Alzheimer's had become a serious disability for her safety. Alexandra, Penelope and I had reached our limits of being able to care for her at home, even with some professional visitors who helped with her personal care. For me, the most difficult period was as she became aware that she was losing parts of thinking. It was difficult for my sisters and me, as we watched the changes and knew that there was little that anyone could do to stop the progression of the disease. I was truly grateful that I loved her and that we had this slow period of being together while losing each other. Some of the symptoms we had observed more frequently with time included: forgetfulness of events or about her own personal history, feeling frustrated, angry or withdrawn, confusion about where she was or what day it was, needing help to choose appropriate clothing for the season or event, trouble controlling her bladder or bowels, changes in her sleep patterns, such as restlessness at night and sleeping during the day, increased incidents of wandering and becoming lost, and personality and behavioral changes including suspiciousness and delusions or compulsive, repetitive behavior.

Athena's move to Landmark Senior Living Communities, Memory Care Unit

Finally, Athena was admitted as a resident at Landmark Senior Living Communities, Monastery Heights in West Springfield. Athena and I met in our home with the admissions manager for Landmark, who told us, "Memory impairment, from forgetfulness to Alzheimer's disease, can be a very difficult situation to deal with. But at Landmark we know this all too well. We realize that the impairment of memory, at any level, never impairs the spirit or the desire of living a rewarding life."

My wife sat in her green upholstered chair by the window. The cat was curled into a ball, nestled beside her hip. She could feel the gentle purring- the vibrations of satisfaction. But she could not hear, actually with her ears, the sound of the cat. Looking out into the maple tree, Athena saw a blue jay. It was darting from branch to branch. There was a time when Athena's cat would have chased the jay, but the cat had become less interested in chasing birds in recent years. It was almost fourteen years old. Athena could not hear the voice of the blue jay, but she could tell from the bird's rapid movement that he was scolding some animal on the ground below.

I am sure that Athena hoped that her cat would understand the necessary decision. Landmark would not allow any pets, no matter how quiet or docile they might be. A cat is a cat, no exemptions were possible. We had made plans for the veterinary clinic to care for the cat and find a new home.

Athena asked, "What will I be able to bring with me?"

The staff person replied, "You will be able to choose what you wish to bring, just as long as it all fits into your room without crowding. Our policy allows you to have your own dresser, bedside table, easy chair and television. There is some wall space with mounted hooks for several pictures. The window sill has room for some plants or knickknacks. The ample closet includes shelf space and floor space. I'm afraid that we can't store anything more for you than will fit into your room." As long as the manager stood directly in front and spoke clearly, Athena could understand all she said. She was alert during this conversation, although other times she would be confused and not as alert.

"When will I know which will be my room?"

"Your new room became vacant last week and will be ready for you within the next week. It is fortunate that you put your name on the waiting list two years ago."

A few days later, I drove Athena to Landmark so she could see her new room before moving. Her eyes were both curious but somewhat anxious. It was a big decision for both of us. Ever since our marriage we had lived in the same house and had never been apart. Our love for each other had grown deeper through the years. But I knew with both my head and my heart that this would be best so that Athena could receive round-the-clock care. Sometimes it is hard to let go; but love guided me in this decision. I was certain that she would be happy once she adapted to the new place.

"Well, I never expected to move here. I was advised that it is good to have several alternatives for housing planned so that I would have some choices." We walked down the hallway to the room. It was neat and clean and completely empty. The only furniture was a hospital bed and a metal chair. The sink was the only plumbing in the bedroom with a door leading to the private bathroom. The drapes were wide open, letting the warm sunshine onto the pink wall and the brown linoleum.

I asked, "I'm afraid my wife might slip on the floor without a carpet. Should we bring a rug?"

The manager said, "You could bring a small rug, but that is risky for tripping and causing a fall. Wall to wall carpeting is not permitted."

I asked, "Why is that?"

"It is harder to clean carpets than to clean linoleum. This is a new skid-proof type of flooring."

I asked, "Instead of keeping a TV in her room, could she give her set to the lounge down the hall?"

"That would be a wonderful idea if it's in good working condition. That way your wife can share and enjoy the programs with the other residents."

There are eighteen rooms in the Memory Care unit. After we met a few of the residents and saw the rest of the facility, Athena and I drove back home. Several days later she moved in. She adapted quickly and happily to her new home, despite the changes in her setting and neighbors.

At Landmark, there was a routine of a daily schedule for all the residents. Each day of the week included specific activities, such as exercise, wellness, bank and shop, bingo, matinee films, walkers group, programs led by visitors with music, happy hour, and clergy who provided Christian or Jewish worship services. Because all residents were welcome, Athena often attended the Catholic mass offered by the priest, or watched Chalice of Salvation on TV.

The highlights of this program included specially trained staff, individualized service plans designed and supervised by the wellness team, personal care assistance with bathing, dressing, grooming and toileting, self-administered medication management, three nutritious meals per day plus snacks, hourly safety checks, pet, music, dance and art therapy, specially adapted homelike setting, secure indoor and outdoor common areas, coordination of podiatry, lab services, pharmacy delivery, and services provided by visiting nurses, physical and occupational therapists.

The program director at Landmark told me that "the Landmark Memory Care MorningStar Program offers a bright environment, designed from inception, to limit confusion for residents. Contrasting color schemes identify boundaries. All areas are secure for the resident's safety. The professionally trained staff fills the day with activities geared toward creating a sense of purpose, success, and independence. Residents live independently, but in a supervised, neighborhood setting. MorningStar provides a model of care that can help delay functional decline, improve quality of life, support dignity and provide comfort at all stages of one's disease."

For several years, my sisters and I attended the annual Purple mass at St. Michael's Cathedral, where we prayed for a cure for Alzheimer's disease. Music was usually provided by the St. Michaels Cathedral Gospel Choir. A frequent scripture lesson was the mission of the twelve disciples, described in Luke 9: 1-6: "Then they set out and went from village to village proclaiming the good news and curing diseases everywhere." The annual mass was sponsored by the Knights and Ladies of St. Peter Claver. The concluding prayer of the mass declared: "May our faith in You grant us a cure and prevention of Alzheimer's disease in all its forms. May all those experiencing Alzheimer's disease experience Your cure, O Lord God, and may You bless us with a prevention of dementia in all forms. In Jesus' name we pray. Amen."

For the next five years, we had a regular routine while Athena lived at Landmark. Since I could trust the staff at the center, each weekday I would work all morning into the mid-afternoon. At dinner time I would visit her while she ate so I could assist her with her eating, and visit for a couple hours after her dinner. I continued this pattern of visiting almost every day, even long after she had stopped recognizing that I was her husband. I would often tell her: "You are beautiful. You are brave. You are kind and brilliant. I am happy to be your husband. I love you." She would look back at me and smile. I was comforted that she was not afraid or anxious and that she was not in pain.

I did not show in my face or words that I, on the other hand, was often worried and sad about her. At home I cried because I missed my wife terribly; but I did not cry in her presence. I cried more in the years that she was at Landmark and I was home alone than in all the years of our life before. I cherished the memory of our long and loving marriage and our mutual relationship of caring for each other, raising Michael together and then living for all the years after his death. Those memories, and our constant love, encouraged me each day. I missed our daily companionship, conversations, activities together. I missed her hugs and being loved by her.

Although she remembered less and less, my mind recalled more and more about all that we had been through together. Many periods when she spoke and described some experience in the past and she believed she was living in that time, I would identify and share the experience with her as if we were back in those same moments together.

With her full time care being provided by the staff at Landmark, I was able to develop some other activities by myself right after work or after my visit with her. After the several years of caring for her at our home, I had learned that caring for myself was also important. She gradually lost her memory of each member of our family, forgetting our names and our shared histories. She lived more and more in the moment, or in her own memories that usually were about happy times. She especially could remember music and songs, such as church hymns, liturgical responses and Greek phrases. Athena declared that she loved me, but she could not remember my name and anything about our lives together. Often someone at work would ask me "Why do you continue to visit Athena when she no longer knows you?" I always responded to this question: "But I still know who she is and I love her."

Through these years, I learned about positive and developing approaches to the care of persons with dementia. I learned about the different types and symptoms of dementia. I became aware of the relation of dementia to delirium and depression in complex care situations, the symptoms of various forms of dementia, and steps of assessment, treatment and care. I studied about what is happening in the brain with new behaviors, changes in reactions, different language comprehension, the ability to process and use sensory information.

I learned how to describe and define terms such as dementia, Alzheimer's disease, vascular dementia, Lewy Body Dementia, Frontotemporal Dementia (FTD); the key differences between dementia and forgetfulness; the changes in the brain that result in typical changes of behavior and function; and common behaviors that are symptoms of dementia in the areas of memory, understanding, language use, movement and impulse control.

In 2016, I read some research by Harvard University neuroscientist, Dr. Rudolph Tanzi, about Alzheimer's. Dr.Tanzi studied chromosome 21 which is the smallest chromosome. People with Down Syndrome have an extra copy of chromosome 21 in every cell. Those with this extra chromosome often will develop the plaques and tangle in the brain associated with Alzheimer's. He found the gene and it became one of the primary targets for Alzheimer's drug research. Other genes produce amyloid, the plaque associated with Alzheimer's, but not the other primary characteristic of the disease: the neurofibrillary tangles that kill brain cells. Research had discovered that amyloid causes the tangles. Inflammation results from the plaque and tangles and sets the brain on fire. The inflammation is the feature which activates the cognition impairments. Regularly, I have kept informed about new research and new approaches for diagnosis and treatment. All of this gives me hope for people in the future.

Virginia Morgan's life and her work at Santorini Greek Restaurant

After Athena had been living at Landmark for a few years, a new customer visited our Santorini Restaurant and ordered lunch at the counter. It was near closing time and I was cleaning up the grill area. Penelope took her order and I cooked it. After some small talk while eating her lunch, she said, "My name is Virginia Morgan. May I share some of my life story?"

"Sure", I replied. "I am Alexander. I own a share of this place so no one is going to tell me to get back to work. And this is my sister who also owns her share and usually works as a manager or waitress."

Virginia continued, "I was born in Springfield in 1984 and have lived here all my life. I grew up in the Hill-McKnight district in a Victorian style house. Several of the streets are named after Ivy League schools such as Harvard, Princeton and Yale. During my youth I dreamed of attending one of those schools. But in high school, I applied to several Ivy League schools and was not admitted to any of them. But I was admitted to Springfield College. While I was studying there, my parents and two brothers moved to Maryland, so I no longer could live at home. As an African American woman I joined two college groups for women of color. After four years, I graduated in the class of 2006 with a major and teaching certificate in Phys Ed. I was very happy for all that I learned and did there."

She resumed, "That summer I met Louis, who had just returned from his second tour with the Air Force in Afghanistan with an honorable discharge and disability of PTSD. After a few months of dating, we moved in together to share the costs of an apartment. For two years I taught Phys Ed and coached girls' softball and basketball at Putnam High School; Louis worked for a construction company. All was going well until we both lost our jobs in 2008 as a result of the Great Recession. With the cutbacks in public school budgets I was one of the last hired, so one of the first let go."

"The following year, Louis decided to move to Florida to find work in the warmer weather. I chose to remain in Springfield. Our relationship came to a sudden end. He had owned the one car we shared and he drove that to Florida. I could not pay the rent alone. In 2012, after failing to locate another roommate to help with expenses, I lost the apartment and became homeless. Although I was satisfied living in the city I had no family around who could take me in. Within two years I had gone from having a home, a boyfriend and a job to being without a home, a boyfriend and a job. I could not afford a car so I got around the city by walking or by the PVTA bus."

Virginia continued, "For the next few years I stayed in the emergency shelter, lived various places outdoors around the city, and stayed temporarily with friends who offered me some space. I became a client of Friends of the Homeless which operates the largest emergency shelter for adult individuals in western Massachusetts"

I asked her, "What can I do to help you? We are a business and not a social service agency helping the homeless."

She replied, "In addition to providing emergency shelter for adult men and women, Friends of the Homeless also owns and operates a resource center and manages 110 low income housing units on their Worthington Street campus. All FOH shelter and housing is supported by case managers who aim to help the client find and maintain permanent housing. My goal is to find work and permanent shelter."

"One of the conditions of living in the low income, single room occupancy efficiency apartments on Worthington Street is that I have to be employed. In short, would you be able and willing to hire me to work here in your restaurant?"

I told her, "Let me think about it. Come back next week and I will give you an answer. And please give me the contact person at the shelter whom I can call as a reference."

After getting a positive reference about her, Penelope, Alexandra and I agreed to hire Virginia as a waitress. It turned out to be a good decision. She was reliable and responsible and related well with the customers, my sisters and me.

About a month after Virginia began working for us, during a slow time at work, she told me this story: "One of my friends came to the Friends of the Homeless Shelter after he had lost everything from gambling and alcoholism. It had taken him a long time to lose everything: family, house, job, car, dignity and self-respect. While unemployed and living on the streets, he struggled in and out of treatment. He spent all his scarce resources and became addicted by the excitement of gambling and the hope of winning, but always lost. I had learned that the casino is a mixed blessing and curse. It is a blessing by providing income for the workers during construction and then as staff once it opened. But gambling is also a curse on the poor who spend their meager income with the hope of getting rich quick."

I told Virginia, "I have always believed in Lady Hard Work rather than Lady Luck, and have avoided any games of chance. I have also known many friends who have gone into a downward spiral with many issues and problems that worked together against getting and keeping a steady job. Addictions of many kinds are often a central part of the problem. I have seen many situations where the addiction brings down not only the gambler but the entire family."

Virginia continued, "Once homeless, my friend began to drink more because he was depressed. But I know that dependence on a substance to resolve problems never works. My friend eventually accepted his addiction as an illness. One day at a time, he learned to love and accept himself, and stopped gambling and other destructive activities. With the support of others, including our local treatment centers and the resources of the Friends of the Homeless, he is now on his journey of recovery."

On another day, Virginia wanted to discuss what the restaurant could do to help homeless people with their food needs. "Can we give leftover food at the end of each day that will be thrown out, to the homeless?"

I responded, "Public health regulations prevent us from giving away leftover food. It is important to realize we are a private business, not a human services agency. However, I do recommend those who are needing food and cannot pay to the Open Pantry and food programs around the city. I have an information fact sheet which I give to help such persons. It is difficult to set such boundaries since I do care and I want to help. But such practices are to the mutual benefit of my business and their dignity. But I do have another suggestion of what we can do here."

Virginia said, "And what is that?"

"We could have a Pay It Forward coupon board. Customers could make an anonymous cash donation, write out a coupon of the value they have given towards a meal and beverage, with a dollar amount. They can post the coupon on the board. Then we can keep a container that contains the cash donations near the cash register. The individual in need can bring the coupon to the register when ordering and we can pay for the meal for that person as an anonymous gift from one of our other customers. How do you like that idea?"

"That sounds like a good idea. Little acts of kindness. Some people can give, so that others can receive. I can help get the system started. Thanks for your solution to my concern."

I said, "It is not my original idea. I have heard of other restaurants around the country doing the same thing. It is a good idea. So let's go ahead."

Later, in late September 2018, Virginia told me, "As a proud African American I went to the annual Stone Soul picnic last weekend at Blunt Park. It is considered the largest African American festival in New England, with events from Friday evening until Sunday evening. Saturday morning I enjoyed the breakfast of grits, bacon, sausage, scrambled eggs served at the Pavilion. It was a partially cloudy day with a cool, light breeze. There was an encampment of Buffalo Soldiers, who had set up tents, mess hall and grilled food. There were several vendors promoting or selling different products. There were Native American and African American drummers. Saturday evening I stayed for the exciting program of music."

During another conversation at work, Virginia told me, "As a young girl I loved playing basketball on the courts in the city parks or in school, playing for the pleasure and the physical exertion, and engaging with teammates and friends. My time at Springfield Collee and then my first job as a high school physical education teacher and coach filled me with joy, plus an income. Recently, the shelter provided for a small group of us to visit the Basketball Hall of Fame. During the visit we had fun while also being inspired as we learned about many of the Hall of Fame awardees: the players, coaches, supporters of the game at all levels of high school, college, professional, national and international, and Olympics."

I told her, "I enjoyed visiting the Hall of Fame although I have usually not had the time to watch basketball games. Your enthusiasm is contagious. Maybe I will try to take the time for my own recreation. Work has been most of my life. Time to take some time off and enjoy. Thanks!"

She said, "The visit helped me recall many of the positive memories and experiences of teaching. At the Hall of Fame, we could broadcast a game for TV or comment on play by play while watching the video of an actual game. We also could compare or contrast our own bodies with the professional athletes, measuring their wing span, hand size, foot size, height, or skills. On the court at the lower level of the hall, we could shoot baskets or play one-on-one. As a teacher I always loved being able to give life lessons of teamwork that are part of the game of basketball."

I responded, "In a similar way, I see being a business owner and cook as an opportunity to teach values of life. That is why I like to have some of the rules posted on the wall here, such as the **Bill of Rights of the U.S. Constitution**, and teachings of courtesy and respect for one another. "

Virginia told me the story about how James Naismith invented basketball in Springfield, to keep his young male students active indoors during the winter season. Now it is one of the most popular sports around the world.

Virginia continued, "Although I have gotten out of practice, playing at the Hall of Fame revived my sense of achievement and hope for the future. I could still sink baskets, and enjoyed sharing the basketball with others from the shelter. I returned back to the shelter with some thoughts for my personal goals. I met with my counsellor for her guidance. To augment my income I thought about getting another job along with working here at the restaurant. Working at the hall as a host or guide would combine my background as a teacher and a coach, helping with the visitors."

A few days later, Virginia had an interview to work at the Hall of Fame. She called me to report, "Alex, I have been hired to begin parttime work immediately. I will continue my scheduled shifts at the restaurant and work with them around my duties at Santorini."

I replied, "Congratulations! I knew that you could do this. It has been a pleasure assisting, but it is your personality, your experience and your skills that got you the job!"

"I thank you for all that you have done. I learned from working with you to gain back my self-confidence and recall my good work habits. The two jobs will give me more income and job security. I have also begun to exercise and to eat healthier foods."

On June 5, 2018, the world famous and popular food journalist Anthony Bourdain died of suicide. His addiction to heroin, cocaine and alcohol during his early career continued to be a struggle throughout his life. His work made me proud to be a cook and have food at the center of my life and work. His death reminded me of the pain that can be hidden from the public and can result in suicide despite outward appearances of joy and delight. His death reminded me to do what I can to listen, to love and give support to anyone in my conversations.

Events of 2019

Virginia Morgan achieved one of her major goals towards independent living. Besides writing her a reference letter for her application to work at the Basketball Hall of Fame, I also wrote a reference letter when she applied to resume high school teaching. In the summer of 2019, she was offered a full time position to return to Putnam High School in late August as a physical education teacher and coach. Of course, Virginia accepted the contract with great enthusiasm! She planned to continue working part-time at the Hall of Fame, but gave up work with our restaurant. I was happy that I had been able to provide some advice and support while she had been homeless and that, by her efforts, she had become able to live on her own income.

In September 2019, the physician on the Landmark staff observed some new problems with Athena. He had her admitted to Mercy Medical Center for some tests. The medical tests revealed that she had final stage pancreatic cancer. The doctor explained to me that this type of cancer was very aggressive and that there was little that could be done to slow or stop its progression. With the side effects which would occur with either radiation or chemotherapy, he explained that the quality of her life would diminish. He described to me the several options possible, and with that information, I accepted his recommendation that no medical treatment or intervention be applied. I agreed that Athena return to her room at Landmark and receive palliative hospice care there until the end of her life. She would receive medication to keep her comfortable. At her stage of Alzheimer's she was not able to speak or understand anything about her cancer or the prognosis and her imminent death. She continued to be comfortable in her familiar surroundings, with daily care provided by the wonderful staff. I continued to visit her every day, even more often than previously because I had stopped working at the restaurant. I was able to be with her, comfort her and, as our marriage vows had declared, "love her in sickness and in health until death do us part." On December 10, with both of her sisters, spouses and some of their children surrounding her bed, Athena died in her sleep. She was now one of the cloud of witnesses.

After the wake a few days later, the beautiful funeral liturgy was held in St. George Cathedral. Her body was placed in the ground at Oak Grove Cemetery alongside our son Michael and my parents. It was a bitter cold day with high cirrus clouds moving steadily across the sky. The branches on all of the trees were bare, except for the pine trees and other evergreen bushes. I had one more reason to visit this cemetery as long as I could into the future. Again, our family and I were surrounded by *agape* and *philoxenia*, the love and hospitality of our church and community friends. Our church family provided the reception at our Greek Cultural Center.

As for my life odyssey, I continued to cook and work at Santorini, but took more time off. I began to enjoy my life beyond the work that had shaped my entire life. Over the years, we had trained my sisters, my sisters' spouses and adult children, my nieces and nephews, to manage our restaurant. Our family business had been designed so that each person who was an adult owned an equal share. This pattern would continue with the next generations. All of our family members would continue our Santorini Greek Restaurant into the future."

"*Kali orexi*". "Praise be to God, the Father and the Holy Spirit. Amen."

THE GARDENER IN THE ROSE GARDEN

SPRINGFIELD | 2015

I drove to Forest Park about a mile from our home. It was a warm, sunny June morning in 2015. Our children, Mark and Marie, were in school. My husband, David, was away for a week on a business trip as a tax accountant. He wasn't due back for two more days

I was feeling lonely and sad. I missed him. But even more, I was sad because recently when he has been home, we have not been talking very much. I was afraid that we were drifting apart.

I parked the car and sat down on a bench facing the neatly-ordered rose garden in a secluded area of Forest Park. I wanted to be somewhere outside but quiet. Away from the pre-school children and their mothers playing in the playground, and away from the softball fields. The rose garden was the perfect place to be alone with my own thoughts. The white trellis with climbing roses and gravel walkway. Warblers and sparrows chirping in the pine trees. Flying grasshoppers, cherry trees, rhododendron bushes, large birch trees. I needed to get out of the house where there were plenty of distractions and chores to be done. I wanted to get in touch with my feelings.

Last year, David and I had attended a wedding in this rose garden. The couple looked so bright and fresh, just like how I remember our own wedding seven years ago. But time seemed to have tarnished our brightness. I wanted some magic spell that would polish the sheen and brighten our marriage again.

I thought to myself, "I wish I knew what to do about David and me."

Although I had not seen anyone in the garden, suddenly an older woman peered at me from behind the bushes at the end of the rows of rose plants. She was wearing baggy jeans, a plaid-checkered blouse and a white kerchief over her head. A few strands of gray hair shook loose over her forehead, almost covering her blue eyes. Tentatively, she waved at me and slowly came over to the bench where I was sitting.

"Excuse me, but you seem worried about something. Would you care to talk about it."

I replied, "Well, it is just something personal. I didn't know that you were here."

"I am the gardener. I am taking care of the roses. My name is Gardenia."

"That's appropriate. Since you are working in the garden."

"My mother's favorite flower was the gardenia. But my favorite flowers are the roses."

"I'm Julia", I introduced myself. "My husband is away for the week. I came here to think about what is going wrong in our relationship. We seem to be drifting apart. When we were first married and David had to go away, he would call me every night. Now he goes away and rarely calls me. I miss that."

"Have you told him that you miss his calls?"

"I did once, and he called more often the next couple of trips. But then he stopped. He said that after his day of work he is too tired to call me."

"Did you ever call him from your home when he was finished with his day's activities?"

"Well, no. By then, I was too busy taking care of Mark and Marie with their meals and then bedtime."

Gardenia suggested, "Maybe you could make the time to call him. If you miss his voice, you don't have to wait for him. You can call first. You can also have your children talk with him about their day. And when you call, don't nag or complain. Just tell him how you are feeling, that you miss him and want to talk before going to bed."

"I never thought of my calling him, I always waited for his call. I will try that his next trip."

"Marriage is like tending the flowers. It takes patient love and care. It takes getting down into the soil and re-working the soil sometimes so that the roots get properly nourished."

"You mean I have to do something to help?"

"Both of you need to work at your marriage to keep it alive and flourishing. But you can take care of the soil by making sure that you are well nourished and watered."

"You mean like taking better attention to myself? How I dress and look?"

"Somewhat. Julia, you need to love yourself, feel confident and secure in yourself."

Gardenia continued, "Marriage is like a rose. There are seasons when it is cold and there doesn't seem to be any life above ground. But the plant is just resting and gathering strength for the spring. Of course, marriage can have short winters that don't have to correspond with the seasons of nature. When there is no apparent growth in the branches, no leaves and no blossoms, the roots are still sturdy and alive underground."

"Roses needed to be pruned to remove the dead stalks and encourage new stalks to emerge. The metaphor of pruning is not exactly literal. But in a relationship sometimes old issues or memories need to be let go so new experiences can grow. Past grievances and resentments need to be let go. Roses need regular attention throughout the season. They cannot be neglected or stalks will get long and not grow blossoms."

I observed in the garden that the roses ranged from white to yellow, all shades from pink to deep red, small blossoms and large blossoms, The American Beauty and Cape primrose, ramblers and climbers, hybrid teas and perpetuals. Some of the scented species were labelled: *Rosa centifolia*, the cabbage or Provence rose; *Rosa damascene*, the damask rose; *Rosa gallica officinalis*, the French rose.

Gardenia said "With floribundas, I study the difference between strong, medium and weak growths. For strong growth I cut back to about six buds. Cutting back to two buds among the weak stalks encourages the production of sturdier shoots later in the year. All the old or diseased growth among the plants must be cut out in the early spring. Late spring is the time to prune the climbing "sports" or long shoots."

"I water the plants if there has not been a regular rain, water is needed in the soil for growth. Not too little water or too much water. Water, sun and soil are all needed in a balanced way. There are some diseases that attack the plants: mildew, rust. Insects such as Japanese beetles and aphids eat the plants."

Near the bocce court, we were interrupted by the sounds of the zoo and the outdoor children's playground. The cawing of a crow, the screech of a peacock, the roar of a big cat. A toddler ran by, running on the tips of his toes, exuberant with his grandmother. A young mother walked by pushing her infant in a stroller, the rippling sound of the wheels through the gravel. An older child ran from the long slide to the serpentine slide then climbed the rope ladder. "Daddy, look at me!"

Interrupted, Gardenia changed the subject, asking "Julia, do you see a counsellor?"

"No, we can handle our problems all by ourselves. We don't need outside help."

"Actually, it sounds to me like you want all the help you can get. Talking with a counsellor isn't a weakness. It is admitting that you want your relationship to get better. You and David may benefit from talking with a professional to gain some understanding of what you can do to strengthen your marriage."

At that moment, an elderly couple walked along the path among the roses, holding hands. I said, "That's another thing that I miss. We don't hold hands much anymore."

"Well you can reach out and try. Do you take the initiative?"

"No, he usually took the first initiative and then he stopped. I haven't asked why. I don't know."

"Julia, you need to communicate that you like that attention and closeness. But you don't have to wait for his action. You can reach out. If you are rejected, then you can share with him how you feel."

"A rose bush isn't grown in a day. It takes years to grow a bush until it is ready for the rose blossoms to emerge and bloom. In the same way, it takes time to renew a marriage. Both the rose bush and the marriage take work in many little ways.

I continued, "Before the children were born, we used to go out for dinner and dancing. Now it is a major project to coordinate an evening free with a babysitter."

All of a sudden, I realized that it was time for me to get back home before my children got back from school. I thanked Gardenia for her advice and drove back home just in time to be inside. They both rushed in after school. Mark was excited and showed me the papers from his backpack. Marie had some drawings to show me.

"That is good!"

"Guess what it is."

"Is it a cow?"

"No, it's a horse. "

"That is a good-looking horse."

Mark asked, "Mommy, what did you do today?

"Mark, I did some errands and then I went to Forest Park. I had a nice talk with a woman gardener in the rose garden."

He responded, "A woman? The only gardener is old Joe Maquire. He takes care of the roses by himself. There are some others who help with the trees and grass, but he is the only one who takes care of the roses."

"That is strange. I know that she was the rose gardener. And she was definitely not Joe Maquire."

After some snacks, Mark and Marie went outside to play in the back yard.

I called the park office on my cell phone, "May I speak with your gardener who takes care of the roses?"

The office secretary replied, "He is not working today. He is home sick with a cold."

"Did you have a substitute taking his place today?"

She said, "No, there really is no decent replacement for Joseph."

Puzzled, I thanked her and hung up. I looked out and watched the children playing.

At that moment, the phone rang. The caller ID showed that it was my husband. "Hi, David? I was just thinking about you."

"Honey, I've got good news!"

"What is it?"

"My meetings for tomorrow have been cancelled. I can be home in two hours. I would like to take you out for dinner tonight. Are you able to get a babysitter on such short notice? My flight on American Airlines arrives at Bradley at 6:15."

"How about I bring the children and we all can eat out together in Enfield? And then I can get a baby sitter for tomorrow night and we can have dinner for the two of us then?"

David answered, "That sounds like a good compromise. And tomorrow we can go somewhere fancy and we can go dancing afterwards. Perhaps you can wear your red dress."

Although David could not see my smile, I was sure he knew that I was happy by this change in plans.

"Honey, I will see you at the arrival area. I will park in the garage and we will come in to the terminal. I love you."

"I love you too. See you soon."

Before I called Mark and Marie inside, I wondered again to myself. Who was the lady gardener?

TIA SANTIAGO'S SENIOR YEAR OF HIGH SCHOOL

SPRINGFIELD | 2017-2018

Summer 2017

"Hi, my name is Tia Santiago. I just moved into the house next door to yours. Although I miss my friends, I am happy to be living here." Tia had bright brown eyes and turquoise-framed glasses. She was short but athletic looking, wearing a green jersey and white shorts. Enthusiastically, she greeted the elderly woman who had slowly opened her front door.

The woman smiled and replied, "Well, hello my dear. I am Mrs. Carlson. Would you like to come in?" "Sure", Tia answered as she entered the front hallway of the red one-story wooden frame house settled between several tall cedar trees.

Leaning on a travel walker, the woman led Tia into the living room. Mrs. Carlson said, "I'm sorry it takes me a while to move around and get to the door. What grade are you in?"

"I just finished my junior year in Sturbridge and I will be a senior here in September."

Mrs. Carlson asked, "Why did you move here?"

"Because my parents wanted to get jobs in Springfield. I just finished classes at Tantasqua Regional High School in Fiskdale last week. My parents had bought our house and moved most of our things here a month ago to begin work here. I stayed with my best girlfriend and finished my final exams at school. My boyfriend and I decided to go our separate ways since I am moving away, and we parted as friends. I am just starting to learn about Springfield and this neighborhood."

"It is so nice to have a visitor. It isn't often that someone comes to see me. I sold my car since it was difficult driving. My health keeps me from going out much. The hardest part about the summer for me is the heat and humidity."

"Mrs. Carlson, I haven't met any of my new neighbors. You are the very first."

"To be honest, I don't know too many of them myself. Even though I moved in a year ago. I miss the family who had lived in your house. They were my only friends on the street." Mrs. Carlson stood six feet tall and was overweight, wearing a comfortable long floral pattern dress with her white hair in a bun.

Tia said, "Maybe we could help you. My mother can buy groceries for you when she goes shopping. I could get your mail from the mailbox at the end of your driveway, so you wouldn't have to walk out there."

The woman asked, "That would be very helpful. What do your parents do?"

"We moved here because of the many job opportunities with the construction of the MGM Casino. Dad learned that there will be thousands of good paying union construction jobs. After he got out of the Army he has been working in construction so he already has many of the necessary skills. He is a plasterer and cement mason and bricklayer."

"In their new jobs, Mom and Dad, Juan and Rosa, both work the same hours Monday through Friday. They drive back and forth to work together in Dad's 2012 Chevrolet Silverado Crew LT Z71. It is a white 4x4 that he has used as his work truck and our only family vehicle which Mom also drives. Because it has crew seats our entire family can ride in it. He takes good care of it and I love it because it has stereo and a CD player."

"They were able to be hired right after we moved. Mom had worked as an accountant with a large corporation in Worcester. She was hired by the casino as an accountant in the business department during the construction phase. My folks helped the casino reach its hiring goals since they are both Puerto Rican. Dad is also an Army veteran and Mom represents the female gender. Moving into the city, they also qualified as local residents."

"That sounds like they have found steady work really fast. I think I will enjoy having you as neighbors. Since I have lived here I have not met many people. My partner, Edith, died last year shortly after we settled here from Ware. Since then it has been lonely for me. We had lived together for thirty years. But we were not able to get married until the U.S. Supreme Court ruled on June 26,2015 that it was unconstitutional to prevent same-sex couples from marrying in any state. That was an important date for many people around the country! With Edith gone, now that I live by myself, I feel as if most people around here don't have time for a single senior citizen."

Tia said, "I like the way your smile lines show up when you say that."

"Smile lines is a good name for them. I've earned every one of them. I call them my "crinkle-wrinkles". I am almost eighty-two years old," smiling even more broadly.

Tia looked out the window, gazing across the yard at her own new home, a similar style of one-story ranch house although Tia's house was painted blue with white trim.

"A penny for your thoughts."

Coming back to attention, Tia looked at Mrs. Carlson and said, "I think we both need the same thing. To learn more about our neighbors. My sophomore and junior years at Tantasqua, I helped write our student newspaper. I like to write. Maybe we could start a newsletter about the people and activities on our street. Then both of us could learn about each family on Windham Court without being rude or nosy. Just being reporters."

Nodding in agreement, Mrs. Carlson said, "Well, I could be your first subscriber. Maybe I could give you some information and help. That could be a helpful enterprise, helping strangers on the street become better neighbors and perhaps friends."

For the next hour, the two of them discussed what they would need to start a newsletter. After considering charging a small fee for subscribers, they decided it might be better to distribute it for free, and publish two times a month. Tia agreed that she would write it on the computer that she shared with her parents at home.

Mrs. Carlson apologized, "I can't help with the typing since I only have an electric typewriter. I have not learned how to use a computer. Besides, I have rheumatoid arthritis in my hands which make it uncomfortable to type or write much. And also in my hips and knees which makes it hard to move around."

They decided to work on the paper during the week and then distribute it door to door on Saturday when most people might be at home. They agreed that they would continue planning for the first issue the next morning. Tia left Mrs. Carlson and bounded across the front yards and into her house. After her day of work downtown, her mother was unpacking the last of the moving boxes in the living room.

Tia exclaimed, "I just met the greatest person! Mrs. Carlson! She and I are going to publish a street newspaper this weekend."

"Slow down, slow down. Who is Mrs. Carlson? What is a street newspaper?"

"She lives next door in the red house. It is a newsletter for everyone living on our street. We are going to call it **The Windham Court Journal**. We just have to decide how to print it."

Her mother replied, "That sounds like a good summer project. It might keep you busy during the days while your Dad and I are at work. I would think you could make copies at the library down the street. I would be happy to pay for your printing expenses to get you started."

"Thanks, Mom!" She kissed her mother's cheek. That evening Tia began writing the first articles, and reviewed the to do list that Mrs. Carlson and she had created. The next morning after breakfast and her folks had left, Tia returned next door to share what she had written.

Mrs. Carlson suggested, "to get started we can share something about ourselves. Then our neighbors would get an idea what future articles might be like. The first issue can give people the idea of what our project is and how they can contribute news."

Tia realized that Mrs. Carlson was as excited about this new enterprise as she was herself. Although Saturday was another scorching, hot day, they worked steadily to meet their own deadline. They discussed the drafts of some articles that Tia had printed the night before. Finally, they had two pages completed. Tia went back home to make final pages on her printer. Then she walked the one block over to the Sixteen Acres Library to make some copies. Tia went to the librarian's desk and asked if she could make some copies. Tia and Mrs. Carlson had decided to print one copy for each of the thirteen houses on Windham Court and make a few extra copies for themselves.

Once the librarian read the first issue, she requested that she have one copy. "Perhaps your newsletter can help the library too."

Tia replied, "How could our street paper help the library?"

"Perhaps you could include news about our library activities and resources. One of your neighbors, Mr. Winchester, checks out books every week and he could write about the library programs. He lives at 2 Windham Court."

"Thanks for your suggestion. And thanks for being our first subscriber. It was good to meet you. See you later. Bye."

The librarian replied, "Good to meet you also. Both of us support reading and writing. Your newsletter can serve your readers best by sharing information that they can use to improve their lives. Please let me know any way that we can help you and Mrs. Carlson."

Clutching the handful of newsletters in her hand, Tia left the library. Mrs. Carlson had suggested that Tia go door to door and deliver the papers. "Once you have delivered them then come back and report to me. If no one is home, leave the copy in the front door. It is against the law to put them in the mail boxes with the regular mail."

She met Mr. Winchester and after he read the paper, she asked, "Would you be willing to write a column once a month about the branch library news."

He replied "Yes, I would be happy. I feel like the lightning bug that backed into the moving fan... De-lighted, no end."

"Ha, ha", Tia responded. they both laughed. She was happy to meet some of their neighbors who were at home and glad to have Mr. Winchester as one of their writers.

Here are some of the articles in the first issue, published on first Saturday of the month, July 1:

Co-editors and founders: Mrs. Hazel Carlson and Miss Tia Santiago.

Editorial

Hello, We are starting this newsletter to share with the residents on Windham Court two times a month. We are next door neighbors seeking to share information that you provide. It will be a free newsletter. We will deliver one issue to each home, usually on Saturday through the summer.

Our purpose is to serve you. We will accept any news that you report to us about Windham Court and the nearby area. We will edit some news based on our space limitations. We will only report news with the permission of the person or organization being reported. We wish to respect your privacy so request you do not report anything that you do not wish others to read about. We are only distributing this newsletter to the residents on this street, and not beyond. Please let us know your ideas for articles. We will write news and opinions based on your requests.

We do not plan to report or copy information from other media, unless it has a very local angle. This is your local street newsletter so each article should have some neighborhood angle or interest.

The Editors

* * *

One regular column, Meet Your Neighbor, will be based on an interview with each resident. This first issue gives you an example, about the co-editor:

Meet your Neighbor

Mrs. Hazel Carlson moved to 13 Windham Street last summer. She was a nurse who retired seventeen years ago and had worked in hospitals and as a visiting nurse. Her partner, who was a retired U.S. Postal Service worker, died last year, shortly after they moved to this neighborhood.

Mrs. Carlson has some advice: "Whether you are young or old, you should see a doctor at least once a year and see specialists as needed."

"One good way to stay well is to eat healthy meals, exercise each day and get plenty of sleep."

"Enjoy each day as it comes. Worry about tomorrow when it becomes today."

Mrs. Carlson is my new friend. Her arthritis keeps her inside much of the time. But she enjoys talking on the phone for friendly chats. If you promise not to tell her how you found out, she will be 82 on July 12.

You will learn about the other co-editor (that would be me) in future issues.

Yours, Tia Santiago

This first issue included information about the Springfield July 4th Fireworks at the Riverfront.

It was late afternoon by the time Tia had delivered all of the newsletters. She knocked on Mrs. Carlson's front door and they sat down in the living room. It was hard to believe that it was only two days ago that they had met and began their planning for this new enterprise.

"I have been watching you make your deliveries up and down the street."

"Only two families were not home so I left their issues tucked in their front door. Here is your own copy."

"Thank you, Tia. You have done a good job."

"One person suggested that we send some issues by e-mail to those who wish to have a digital newsletter, rather than a printed copy. That will make it easier in the future to deliver the news. I will put something in the next issue asking for e-mail addresses to be sent to me. But for privacy we will not publish anyone's telephone numbers or e-mail addresses."

Mrs. Carlson asked, "Now, would it spoil your dinner if you had a glass of iced tea?"

Tia perked up, "Not at all. I sure am thirsty. I am glad we have become co-editors."

"And friends." Mrs. Carlson went out to the kitchen and prepared a tray with two glasses of iced tea. Tia carried the tray back to the living room.

As Mrs. Carlson sat down, she picked up her glass and said, "Let us toast to our first day's delivery. And it works both ways. Each of us has gained a new friend. Next week, after the holiday, we can get together and plan our next issue. I have a few more new ideas." She smiled and touched her face alongside her eyes, feeling her own smile lines.

* * *

On July 4th the Santiago family, Juan her father, Rosa her mother and Tia, attended the Springfield fireworks. Tia's older brother Javier, known as Javi, her only sibling, was not able to come for the holiday because of his summer job in Boston. Riverfront Park was very crowded and they found a place to sit on the ground to watch the beautiful fireworks which exploded from the Memorial Bridge over the Connecticut River. There were many men and women who wore Veterans caps or shirts, identifying their branch of military service. Many had fought in World War II, Korea, Vietnam, Afghanistan or Iraq. There was a great spirit of friendliness among all the crowd, whether strangers or relatives, young and old, celebrating Independence Day.

On the next day, Wednesday, Tia walked over to the library to gather some news. She visited the Clodo Concepcion Community Center for some information about their programs. She met the Springfield police officers were who were part of the community policing unit. She talked with them about security and safety issues in the neighborhood for a future article.

During the weeks of her summer vacation, Tia visited several places seeking summer work. But most employers required that their employees be either eighteen years old or have a high school diploma. Most of the employers had already hired their summer employees weeks earlier. She was either too young or too late to find a job. She then looked around to find a part time job to earn some income or serve as a volunteer. She mowed some lawns and did yard work for several neighbors on Windham Court and volunteered at the library shelving books.

Tia attended the monthly Teen Readers Advisory Panel at Sixteen Acres to meet and share ideas about improving library programming for teens, plan events, give input for resources to purchase and other fun activities. She also volunteered at the Goodwill store next to the library. Without a car, Tia learned to ride the PVTA busses to get around the city. Tia walked around the area to learn about the wider neighborhood and environment. When her parents were not working, she would ride with them on errands.

Tia asked the librarian, "What summer program do you have for teens?"

The librarian said, "We have a reading club. The theme is Build a Better World with many activities during the summer. Also, you are encouraged to read anything you like, such as books, comics, manga, magazines or material found on the internet."

"Is this done by individuals or as a group?"

"Well, you can log your individual reading. There are prizes through the summer based on how much reading you have done. After one month of reading you pick out your prize: a book of your choice or a gift card. After eight weeks of reading, you will have earned a second prize, either a book or a gift card. The reading club will end just before school begins."

Tina met another neighbor, Jacki Davis, also a high school senior, while distributing the second issue. Jacki read through the entire issue and responded "I like your idea and the entire paper. I can help gather information from some of our high school classmates. Before school opens you will be able to get to know some who will be our classmates. This newsletter might help young people and older people understand each other better too! I am all for that! Which high school will you be attending?"

Tia replied, "I haven't registered yet for school so I don't know what options I will have."

"Well, I go to Springfield Central High School. I would encourage you to go there. Most of my friends go there. That would make it easier for you to make new connections among our senior class. There are just over two thousand students in grades 9 through 12, with about 400 in our senior class. I like Central because there is a good mix of students both racially and economically. I consider that a good thing."

Tia responded "Yes! Me too. I believe in the value of unity and diversity. Since the 2016 election there have been many incidents against people of different backgrounds."

Jacki said, "Central High reflects the population of the city of Springfield. 51% of the student population are Hispanic and 24% are African American and 17% are white. For 26% of the students English is not their first language. Student achievement ranked recent students relative to their proficiency in a given subject, based on the MCAS tests. The ranking of performance in English Language Arts is 96% at Central compared with the performance in all high schools in Massachusetts. Science at Central is at 72%, compared to the Massachusetts performance of 89 %. And Central High Mathematics is 79% compared to Mass 90%."

Tia responded, "Those are impressive numbers. How do you know them?"

"We studied them as part of our statistics class. Will you be taking the PVTA city bus or a school bus? The city bus stops along Parker Street and has more schedule choices than the school busses. There are stops at each of the city high schools. But If you decide on Central High I can drive you because I have a car and will be driving there myself."

After checking information about all of the Springfield high schools, the next week Tia went with her mother to the Parent Information Center and registered for classes at Springfield Central High School. She brought the transcript of her first three years at Tantasqua Regional High School. She had done very well on the MCAS scores and in several AP courses there. She registered for the courses for her senior year to ensure being able to graduate in June 2018. These included AP Calculus, AP Chemistry, Physical Education, Journalism and Aerospace Science.

In the following week Tia and Jacki got together. Jacki was six feet tall and lean, with short black hair and a bright smile with dimples. She told Tia "I had a boyfriend, Bradley, the first three years of high school. He was in the grade ahead of me, a senior last year. He is attending Lehigh University in Pennsylvania. After he graduated, we mutually decided to break up since he would be so far away and we wanted to be free to make new friends."

Jacki said, "My father works as an auto mechanic on Boston Road in Springfield; my mother works as a teller at Bank of America. They have had the same jobs for years. Both of them are tall, although I am almost as tall as they are. In recent years there's been a lot of yelling between them. My brothers are still at home and they fight a lot. Between school activities and friends as my refuge, I spend as little time at home as possible."

Jacki summarized her family history to Tia. "My paternal grandparents came to Springfield after World War II from Georgia where my ancestors had been slaves until the 1860s. Both my paternal and maternal grandparents settled in Mason Square. My parents owned a home there until my two brothers and I were born. I have lived with my parents all of my life in the same one-story ranch style house on Windham Court."

Jacki and Tia quickly learned that although their home lives were different, they shared many of the same interests. Their favorite musicians were Beyonce, Janet Jackson, Alicia Keys, JLo, Ariana Grande. They both were loyal Democrats who supported Hillary Clinton and then Barack Obama. Their favorite outfits were neat black blouses and pants or blouses with solid bright colors. Both of their parents preferred popular musicians such as Michael Jackson, Smokey Robinson, Aretha Franklin, Gladys Knight, Whitney Houston, Louis Armstrong and Duke Ellington. The two generations of both families enjoyed mostly Latina/ Latino and African American music.

The third week in July, Tia met and interviewed a couple on Windham Court who had come to Springfield as refugees from the civil war in Lebanon. This part of the interview was published in the next newsletter:

> *"We had lived in Sidon, Lebanon, on the Mediterranean coast. First we lived in east Springfield and have lived here on this street for ten years and we have become American citizens. Sometimes when we met our neighbors, or at work, it is assumed that we are Muslims. But we are Christians of the Maronite Rite Catholic Church. We became members of the St. Anthony parish on Island Pond Road. Services are in English and Aramaic, the language of Jesus of Nazareth."*
>
> *"Our church is located close to much of the damage from the tornado that touched down on June 1, 2011. Many of our friends in the parish were affected by the destruction. Our church helped provide space for people to stay and provided food and supplies in the months afterwards. Hundreds of homes were damaged and our church became a local shelter and information center. Out of the destruction and chaos many people stepped up and were helpful to their neighbors."*
>
> *"The government in Lebanon is a Christian-Muslim democracy. Our family wears modern Western clothing. We do not wear Muslim garb of the burka and hijab because we are not Muslim. Our religious traditions have had mutual respect for each other for centuries."*
>
> *"Lebanon was one of the most advanced and peaceful nations in the Middle East. This was all shattered during the civil war and subse-*

quent occupation by foreign forces. Since Lebanon shares its eastern border with Syria it was one of the first nations to welcome refugees from Syria, now amounting to several millions surviving in refugee camps. Lebanon shares its southern border with Israel and has been occupied by Israeli troops and Hezbollah for the past few decades.

"In Lebanon, the Red Crescent (similar to the Red Cross in the United States) was helpful in providing emergency relief. Much of the time in Lebanon we were victims and became refugees ourselves and moved to America. Following the tornado in Springfield, because we lived outside of the path of destruction, we were able to be helpers through our church. We found many new friends here as we cooperated with other churches and relief agencies to bring resources to our community."

After reading this interview article Mrs. Carlson told Tia, "I am Swedish Lutheran and started going to Bethesda Lutheran Church on Island Pond Road, very close to St. Anthony's. But when I gave up my car and driving several months ago, I don't go there anymore."

During the summer, Tia often would prepare dinner at home for her parents when they came home from work. Tia explored several Puerto Rican restaurants, bakeries and food markets around the city. Tia and Jacki, or Tia with her parents, would occasionally go out together to one of these. Their favorites were Palate Restaurant, Borinquen y Quisqueya, El Chicarron, El Morro Restaurant and Bakery, Latino's Kitchen, Mesa Buffet, Mi Antojito Bakery, Puerto Rico Market and Bakery, El Salvador, Raices and Salsas.

During the summer Tia had noticed a group of people Waving for Peace Monday evenings on Wilbraham Road near Parker Street, in front of Foster Memorial Church. She stopped by and joined them and learned they had been doing that every week for three years. All members of the church, they waved at the drivers and passengers coming home from work. Tia joined them a few Monday evenings in the summer. Once school started and she had activities after school, she was not able to continue. On the front lawn there was a Peace Pole with "May Peace Prevail on Earth" in four languages: Tibetan, Spanish, English and Hebrew. Over the front door to the sanctuary was a bright rainbow PRIDE banner welcoming people of the community.

In the middle of August Jacki met with Tia and Tia's parents, Juan and Rosa, at their home to share more about the AFJROTC program at Springfield Central. Tia asked Jacki, "What does AFJROTC stand for?"

Jacki replied, "Air Force Junior Reserve Officer Training Corps. I joined the unit at Central my Freshman year. It was a good way to get to know the other students from all four grade levels. We have four homerooms dedicated to the ROTC program. Each homeroom is filled with trophies earned by ROTC over the years from the local to the national competitions. Aerospace science is taught in each of these classrooms. On the walls of each room are posters and diagrams about aviation history, types of aircraft, and motivational statements for leadership and patriotism."

"We explore the world of civilian, industrial and military aerospace and develop our leadership skills. We discover the historic and scientific aspects of aerospace technology and achieve self-reliance, self-discipline and other characteristics found in good leaders. After high school graduation we are eligible to pursue college studies in a technical or non-technical major. Air Force ROTC also offers scholarships for cadets that will pay most tuition costs for up to three or four years."

Tia's mother asked, "Is it only for students planning to go into the military?"

Jacki said, "No, Mrs. Santiago. Enrollment in AFJROTC does not subject you to a military obligation and is not linked to a recruiting program. Regardless of your chosen career path, it provides tools for success after high school. However, there are benefits available for students wishing to pursue a military path."

Tia asked, "What are your plans after high school?"

Jacki said, "I plan to continue at a college or university. Since I will have been in this JROTC program for four years I may be able to receive credit for a full year of college Air Force ROTC. It someone wants to apply to a military service academy, such as the Air Force Academy, there is a direct application program reserved for qualified AFJROTC cadets. With all other factors being equal such as grades, SAT scores, community involvement, the JROTC experience provides a competitive edge over the rest of the applicants. That is the path I am planning to pursue."

Tia's Dad said, "That's great! Where are you applying?"

Jacki responded, "Although this may change in the next few months, my first primary choice are schools that provide Air Force ROTC. These include the Air Force Academy in Colorado, UMass Amherst, Mount Holyoke, Clark in Worcester and Curry College in Milton. Tia, where are you thinking of applying?"

Tia said, "When I was living in Fiskdale and going to Tantasqua, there was no JROTC program there, so I was not even considering some of the benefits and options you describe. I was thinking of living at home and going to a school near Worcester, like Clark or Worcester Polytechnic. For me, now, I am considering more options then when I lived in central Massachusetts. With more than eleven colleges and universities in this area of the Connecticut River valley, I am still thinking of living at home to save expenses. But we'll see in the next few months. Decisions, decisions."

* * *

During one of Tia's visits in late August to her next-door neighbor, Mrs. Carlson told Tia about her late partner. "Edith had developed severe pain in her back and went to a doctor for medication. He prescribed opioids and they gave her great relief. Several months later, she was found in the park, having fallen. The ambulance came and the EMTs tried to resuscitate her, but she was not responsive. She was already dead. It was a great shock as she had been feeling better from the back pain. A few days after her death, it was determined that she had accidentally overdosed on some street Fentanyl discovered in her system. Edith had become addicted to the opioids. I had not even been aware of it."

"After her death, I read that the epidemic had been growing and that many of the deaths were not publicized or reported. By now there is much more awareness. I feel guilty that I had not been aware that she had become addicted. I could have helped her get treatment and she would still be alive today. There is still a great need for public information and support for those who are addicted and their friends and family."

Tia responded, "I am so sorry to know that that is how your partner died. It must be terrible to have lost your life long partner so suddenly. In my high school the last few years the major problem has been with heroin and alcohol. But I had also known about people beyond their high school years addicted to opioids and many people who had died from overdoses."

Mrs. Carlson continued, "After Edith died, I began to feel very lonely and ate a lot to stuff my feelings. I gained lots of weight in the next few months and lost all interest in anything. There are so many of the objects in our house which continue to remind me of her and our happy days. Our wedding... our new house here, and both of us retiring and finding a smaller place here in Springfield."

"Tigger, my tiger cat, is a big comfort and keeps me company. But she is over twelve years old and sleeps most of the time."

After this visit, Tia suggested to her mother that the family invite Mrs. Carlson over for lunch on a Saturday or Sunday at their home, or take her out for a meal at a restaurant. Her mother agreed and this began a weekly practice that continued for the entire school year.

Learning More About JROTC

Later in August, Tia discussed with her parents her decision to enroll in JROTC. They both supported her decision. Her Dad asked, "Are the cadets assigned to their homeroom based on their grade in high school, or by their year of membership in JROTC?

Tia said, "There are four homerooms assigned for the cadets. Room 105 is for all the Senior cadets which is where I will be assigned as in the Senior class although in my first year of JROTC. They get the weekly briefing so they can brief all the cadets in their class. Room 113 is for all the Drill team Members. Room 129 is for any Junior cadet that wants to be there. Room 110 is for the Color Guard team, choir Team and other younger cadets."

Her mother asked, "Do all the cadets eat lunch in the Cafe, or do they eat in their homeroom?"

Tia replied, "Every student in Central is on the free meal plan. Breakfast is eaten in our homeroom. Lunch is served in the Café. Dinner is also provided for those taking part in our after-school sports and activities. Sodexo is the high school food contractor and they offer the black book bag weekend meal plan to help those students that might have limited food over the weekend."

Tia continued, "Wednesdays are Uniform Day when all cadets wear their uniforms all day. The morning starts with inspections by advanced cadets of the uniforms worn by the younger cadets. Their peers use the inspections as a time to teach and learn the discipline and value of united training. We will also practice drills. I am studying and memorizing the drill manual which we will be following."

Her Dad asked, "What is taught in the Aerospace Science course?"

She replied "Aerospace Science is a one-credit, science elective course that can be taken all four years at Central. It teaches citizenship, self-discipline, followership and leadership skills and patriotism. Classes cover military customs and courtesies, flag etiquette, instruction in marching for parades and ceremonies, study habits, time management, first aid, communications skills, personal counselling and the fundamentals of financial, personal and stress management. The course concludes with a review of aerospace careers."

* * *

At the end of August and later in early October Tia took the SAT Subject tests which had to be completed before application deadlines for colleges by December. She selected up to three subject tests on each test date chosen from among these subjects: Literature, US History, Mathematics Level I, Math Level 2, Biology, Chemistry, Physics, French and Spanish. The results of these tests would be reported in two weeks.

Classes began at Springfield Central High on August 28. Tia rode with Jacki to the campus at Bay Street and Roosevelt Avenue, a practice that they followed during most school days for the rest of the year. In September, Tia attended the Puerto Rican Parade. After the parade, she met a young man from Puerto Rico who had been in an accident on his motorcycle. In an induced coma for months, a bar was put in his spine and he had short term memory loss. Due to his disability which made it harder to play many sports, he trained to become a barber so that he could continue to be around people and earn an income. Because one of Tia's possible career interests was to become a physical therapist, she was inspired by this conversation.

Tia signed up for several clubs at the start of the school year: AF-JROTC, Gender Equality and Newspaper/Journalism. The Newspaper/Journalism Club was responsible for **Central Talon,** the student newspaper. As many of the student staff had been involved in the previous year, most sections of coverage were already selected. Tia agreed to write articles about Central news and community news. There were more than fifty clubs and special homerooms from which to choose. With Senior class events and academic work, Tia decided to select only a few clubs. She knew clubs would be one of the best ways to meet classmates and make new friends.

The entire Senior Class took a field trip in early September to the Basketball Hall of Fame, called "Go Higher". It was sponsored by the Mass Dept of Higher Education, Gear Up and included 29 academic institutions around Massachusetts and all the high schools of Springfield to learn about opportunities after graduation. Tia wrote an article for the **Central Talon** after the day's experience.

* * *

On September 10, Jacki Davis and Tia attended Rally Day and worship at Foster Memorial Church. After worship Tia then met with her parents at Raices Restaurant, one of their favorite Puerto Rican restaurants, located in the South end one block from MGM Casino and Red Rose Pizzeria. Her parents often would eat there for their lunch break or before heading home at the end of the work day. The tables were covered with faux animal skin clothes, the walls and seat covers were burgundy and tan. It was casual dining and usually had several families attending. Tina ordered pina colada, roasted pork shoulder, sweet plantains, yellow rice and beans. Her father ordered conch turnover, chicken stew, seafood rice and mango smoothie. Her mother ordered tuna salad, grilled pork chops and ginger ale.

Tia reported to them about the morning service, "Rally Day welcomed all the children and youth back from summer experiences. Jacki and I were welcomed warmly by the greeters at the door and by several other folks. Pastor Barbara led the worship and preached the sermon. The message in the bulletin declared: "We are a joyful, welcoming, inclusive and supportive community of Christ followers, eager to shine God's love by connecting people through partnerships and service that foster peace and hope in our neighborhood, wider community and world."

"Several worshippers are Puerto Rican or African American, with the majority being white. Several adults with special needs from a nearby group home attended worship. The children were an active part of Sunday worship and other programs during the week."

"During the service the congregation sang "Happy Birthday" to a few people who were celebrating their birthdays this week. And later the congregation was invited to share their personal joys and concerns. During the prayers they prayed for the celebrations and the concerns of several people in the congregation and in the wider community. It was announced that several of the members were helping with the Big E during September by serving food. They announced that later in September there would be a Ziti dinner to benefit Open Pantry's Loaves and Fishes Kitchen. Today, there was an ice cream social served outside after worship."

* * *

On September 20, Hurricane Maria struck Puerto Rico and many other islands of the Caribbean. Because of the devastation of their homes and towns, many Puerto Rican families were evacuated to the mainland, with a large population coming to the greater Springfield area. As part of her leadership in Junior ROTC, Tia helped raise funds, clothing and food to deliver to the families in Puerto Rico who were without power, clean water or basic necessities. By October only 22% of Puerto Ricans had power restored, and one third had no access to clean water.

This is part of the article by Tia published in the **Talon**:

"The devastation of the two hurricanes Irma and Maria across the U.S. territory of 3.3 million of American citizens who live on the island of Puerto Rico, caused thousands of residents to lose power, communications, food and water. We urge you to help with any resources you can provide. The AFJROTC cadets and faculty are collecting supplies to send to Puerto Rico, where many of our relatives and friends live. We are coordinating local efforts with the New North Citizens Council, which is also trying to share the communications from individuals on the island to those who live on the US mainland. We are learning that much of the supplies are not able to be transported to the inland and mountains due to the damage of most roads and the lack of trucks and drivers. It is being reported that the only reliable method of getting relief supplies to the American citizens of Puerto Rico is through the U.S. Postal Service."

Tia attended a rally at Court Square, organized by several of the Spanish-speaking churches, with speakers, prayers and songs of support for Puerto Rico and the Caribbean Islands. She was upset by the tragic effects of the hurricane on most of the island. "I wanted to go as a volunteer but decided that I needed to save my money for after graduation. Also, I did not have the training and skills to be of much help."

For the entire school year, Tia rode to school and back home with Jacki. It worked well because they both were actively involved in most of the same extra-curricular activities. Both of them took part in many of Junior ROTC activities and events so this was convenient. They became very close friends due to similar interests. Many of their friends were also cadets in the ROTC. When they could not ride together, Tia took the PVTA city bus, which involved a couple of transfers.

Fall 2017

Tia wrote an article for **Central Talon** about the CROP Walk for Hunger:

> *"Crop Walk for Hunger on Sunday, October 15 at Trinity United Methodist Church. To raise funds for local and national needs for food and emergency relief and ongoing development.*
>
> *"What are CROP Hunger Walks? Neighbors walking together to raise funds to end hunger in their community and around the world. Together- with different ages, faiths and backgrounds- we raise money and awareness to end hunger, one step at a time. With 1,500 communities across the country walking each year, we are America's Hunger Walk.*
>
> *"CROP Hunger Walks are interfaith events that build community while also making a difference locally and globally. Anyone is able to join! Your participation impacts individuals and families in more than 30 countries. In many developing countries, people walk as many as six miles a day to get food and water. One in nine people worldwide lack access to clean water and a healthy diet. In walking as they walk, our steps take on meaning. We walk to be in solidarity with their struggle.*
>
> *"In the last 25 years, CROP Hunger Walks have raised more than $300 million to help people struggling to feed their families- both*

around the world and around the corner. In fact, up to 25 percent of the funds raised by CROP Hunger Walks benefit the communities where they take place, by supporting local food banks, pantries, community gardens and other hunger-fighting initiatives.

"What is your impact? Here are some examples of what CROP Hunger Walks enable: a community garden for families with a hoe, shovel and seeds; emergency food supplies for a family; biosand filters that help prevent the spread of disease; raised planting beds with nutrient-rich soil and gardening tools; small grants for women to jump-start their businesses; water pumps and training local residents to maintain them for the community"

Tia and Vicki participated with the large group of Springfield Central Junior ROTC cadets, teachers and parents and with the group from Foster Church who also walked.

The JROTC Golden Pink awareness team went to the Springfield Rays of Hope walk on October 29, and blew up all the pink balloons that make the starting point arch. Later in March, they also attended the Springfield Thunderbirds Hockey Team "Pink in the Rink". The cadets took part with the SADD Central Strong club ("Students Against Destructive Decisions"). The SADD team focussed on Teen suicide, teen dating and violence, Texting and Driving and Drinking and driving, smoking, and Alcohol Awareness month. The cadets also participated in the Western Mass "Walk out of the Darkness".

* * *

On November 10, schools were closed to observe Veterans Day. The JROTC Drill team and Color Guard took part in the ceremonies downtown at the Veterans memorials opposite the Symphony Hall. High school academic and after school activities also kept Tia busy during most of the fall semester.

Many of the Sundays in the fall Tia and Jacki worshipped at Foster Church. Foster members collected gently used or new coats, for students at Rebecca Johnson School. In the summer the church annually collected school items ranging from pencils, glue sticks, crayons, colored pencils, pocket folders to back packs distributed to Rebecca Johnson students. In November there was a pancake brunch at the church to raise funds to send for Tenzin's living expenses, the thirteen-year-old Tibetan refugee living at a school in northern India.

Tia told her mother, "I was upset with the delay and neglect of the needs of the people of Puerto Rico. Many Hispanic groups in our region came together to ship supplies and help to the thousands of people there. I also became involved in welcoming some of the families who came to Springfield and Holyoke because of the living conditions and needed temporary housing and schools until the situation on the island improved. I seriously considered going as a volunteer to work in Puerto Rico after graduation. Later I realized that I would need to be independent and not be a burden on the local families."

Tia wrote an article for the **Talon** promoting the second annual Massachusetts College Application Celebration on December 6 held in the school Library throughout the school day. She wrote:

> *"This event will provide one-on-one meetings with admission representatives from multiple in-state colleges and the opportunity to hand out copies of your high school transcripts to the colleges of your choice. This will be for all seniors and is sponsored in collaboration with Gear Up. Participating colleges will include AIC, Bay Path University, Curry College, Holyoke Community College, Johnson and Wales University, Keene State College, Mass College of Liberal Ars, Springfield College, UMass-Amherst, Westfield State University, Western New England University and Worcester State University.*

* * *

In November, Tia spent one weekend with a female friend of her brother Javier in Boston and attended some college activities with them. From Boston, Tia texted her mother:

Tia: Thinking about attending a college in Boston and living near Javier.

Rosa: It is very expensive. He received a full scholarship there.
Tia: I can still apply for financial aid.
Rosa: I would miss you so much.
Tia: Me too. But big brother could watch over me.
Rosa: You have another month to write your college applications.
Tia: Just thinking. No decision now.
Rosa: Let's talk later. Love you.
Tia: Love you too.

* * *

By the end of November, Tia decided not to apply to colleges in the Boston area. She realized that Javier and she would be very busy with their own academic and personal lives and would probably not see each other much. She began to narrow down to colleges in western Massachusetts.

Throughout her entire Senior year, Tina was active in the JROTC program. Tia considered enlisting in the Air Force both for the education and the income promised. This was also being actively considered by many of her Senior cadet classmates, both directly from high school or after college. Her Dad wore his Army veteran cap much of the time and described to her the advantages and disadvantages of the military option. He also joked with her about the Army vs Air Force, but he seriously encouraged his daughter to follow her own journey.

Winter 2017-2018

In December, she completed applications to American International College (AIC), Springfield College and UMass-Amherst. Her first choice for a major and a career was Physical Therapy or Exercise Science which were programs at all of these colleges. Her high school grades at Tantasqua were excellent but she also wanted to focus on her senior year courses and extracurricular activities. She considered applying for work at the casino immediately after high school rather than continue with higher education. She had different experiences and interests that pulled her back and forth in several directions. Several of her close friends wanted her to enroll where they were applying: schools in the greater Springfield area and schools outside of Massachusetts.

Tia wrote an article for the **Central Talon** about Spirit Week, the week just before winter vacation.

> *"Monday Winter White Out Day – students wore white, shirts, pants and shoes. Tues Jersey Day, any type of jersey with regular school pants. Wednesday was Professional Day, no jeans, sweats or leggings. ROTC cadets wore their uniforms. Thursday was Character Day, express a character the student wants to be for the day, jeans only allowed if it has to do with the character. Friday was Ugly Sweater Day and Jean Day."*

The schools were closed December 25-January 1 for holiday vacation. Javi was home for the break so Tia and he spent as much time together as possible, along with time with their parents and her girlfriends. They ate out several times at some of their favorite Springfield restaurants.

Tia had read the **Hunger Games** novels and then went to see all of the Hunger Games films over several years. The series offered an empowering story of fighting against authoritarian control and the power of individual citizens, especially young people, to lead for change. Tia said, "One of my favorite movie celebrities is Jennifer Lawrence. It is hard to realize she is only ten years older than I am and has such a career and good common sense in her life. She is the youngest person to have won four Oscar nominations. I saw **Silver Linings, X-Men, Hunger Games, Red Sparrow** and **Passengers**. With all of her fame and wealth, she seems to have a good head and attitude. Lawrence recently said "I get my happiness from my friends and my house- they've brought me so much sanity." That is true for me too, my friends and my family provide me with my happiness."

Early in January, Tia submitted her Free Application for Federal Student Aid. On January 15, the schools were closed for the Dr. Martin Luther King, Jr. birthday anniversary. Tia and Jacki attended the city-wide celebration at the Mass Mutual Center on Main Street, with several talks and music provided by students from several of the Springfield City schools.

With the applications for college completed and the final semester of her senior year, Tia had more time for AFJROTC activities, volunteering at Sixteen Acres Library and attending Foster Memorial Church.

AFJROTC provided a close-knit community and a shared culture that encompassed many events together. During the school year, the JROTC cadets took part in the following events or locations: Boston Freedom Trail, Shriners Circus, NE Air Museum, Springfield Veteran Day Parade, Puerto Rican Parade, Big-E Parade, Holyoke St. Patrick's Day Parade, Florence MA Memorial Day Parade, Battleship Cove, Flagging of the Graves at Oak Grove Cemetery, Ice Cream Social at the Holyoke Soldiers Home, ringing the bells for the Salvation Army, weekend helping the DAV hand out "Forget Me Nots", collecting soda can tabs to help out the Shriners Hospital, blood drives. In one year, these activities included over 7,000 hours of community service by the cadets.

Spring 2018

Much of the Spring season was fairly light for Tia's school work after the pressure of completing applications to the colleges. The shooting at Margery Stoneman Douglas High School in Parkland, Florida, took place on February 14. Tia took part in the Springfield March for Our Lives on Saturday, March 24 at Court Square. Following the rules of the JROTC program, she took part as an individual citizen and did not wear her JROTC uniform or identify herself as a member of ROTC. This event started with a rally and then a peaceful walk up to the Federal building on State Street. When the group returned to the steps of City Hall there were several speakers from community organizations. Many students from a few of the area high schools also participated. In the weeks after the school shooting there were discussions in some of her classes about ways to make schools safe and secure places. Tia wrote an article for **The Central Talon** about the local rally and the issues related to gun violence.

During the spring Tia continued to spend time with Sarita, who was also a JROTC cadet. Sarita's grandparents had moved to Florida from Cuba when Fidel Castro came to power. Ten years ago her family moved to Springfield. Their family had returned to visit Cuba in 2016 by plane after the economic sanctions had been lifted. She was excited to share her experiences as it was her first trip to Cuba, her ancestral home. Tia interviewed Sarita for an article published in **The Central Talon**.

Tia attended the Easter Sun Rise service followed by a breakfast at Foster Memorial. Her classes and senior activities kept her busy at Central during the spring. Due to these school activities, she had little time to engage with many of the activities at the church but she attended Sunday worship there as often as she could.

The JROTC Annual Military Ball was held in April at the Sheraton Hotel. The female cadets dressed up in formal gowns and the male cadets wore their uniforms with all their medals. It was a sit down formal meal, the young gentlemen stood and pushed the chair in for the ladies, then dancing until 11:00 pm. It was a great opportunity for the cadets to socialize with each other and practice formal manners and etiquette. Both Jacki and Tia with their economic tastes had purchased gently used prom gowns that they could use again at other formal events.

In April, Tia received acceptance letters from the three schools to which she had applied: AIC, Western New England University and Springfield College. Springfield College also offered her a major financial aid award package. Delighted with this news, she wrote to Springfield College and accepted their offer for admission and financial aid.

During the Spring vacation Tia attended the Accepted Students Day at Springfield College. She was able to meet other incoming students, faculty of her planned major and again visit again the campus. Special events were held for prospective Exercise Science, Nursing, Occupational Therapy, Physical Therapy and Public Health students. She visited the health science labs and facilities, performed some lab experience with faculty members, and spoke with current Springfield College students. As part of the Air Force ROTC program at Springfield College Tina would be able to attend ROTC classes at UMass-Amherst as part of Detachment 370.

During the vacation, Tia and her parents went out to lunch at Palate Restaurant, a fairly new place, on Boston Road to celebrate Tia's eighteenth birthday and her acceptance at Springfield College. Tia especially liked the glass wall with water streaming down inside of the wall separating the bar from the full dining area. The high top booths with dark leather seats and brass foot rails were distinctive. First, each of the family decided what they wanted to eat.

After they placed their orders, Tia's father said, "Your mother and I are very proud of your dual accomplishment. Rosa, would you like to give the good news?"

Her mother said "You are now legally an adult, been accepted to your first choice of Springfield College and have received an important financial package from them. We have decided to give you a special gift combining both events. You have decided to live at home during your freshman year as one way to save on housing expenses. Juan, dear, you continue."

Her father said, "After your graduation, we are going to go with you to a car dealer to help you buy a used car in your own name. We will pay for the car payments. You will pay for insurance, maintenance and your gas usage."

Tia responded, "Wow! That is amazing! I am totally surprised. I love you both so much!"

Rosa and Juan together said "We love you so much too!"

Her mother said "You have worked hard and earned this gift! We had expected to be paying for most of your college education."

Juan added "But when you received the news two weeks ago of the financial aid package that gave us the freedom to help you with your transportation."

Their lunch soon arrived and their celebration continued. For appetizers they shared some handmade potato balls filled with marinated beef and stuffed plantain baskets with pork. For the main course each of them enjoyed different large platters. Tia's Dad, Juan, had traditional Spanish Paella with a mixed veggie, seafood and pork infusion in a mofongo basket. Her mother, Rosa, had sautéed beef steak with onions and peppers, served with morro rice and sweet plantains. Tia had slow cooked chicken breast in a sauce with fresh herbs, served with house rice, beans and sweet plantain. It was a delicious meal.

After the earlier big announcement, they talked about each other's activities, work and studies. Tia and her family continued to collect relief supplies for families in Puerto Rico, especially those living in the mountains, still suffering from hurricane Maria. Now that she was eighteen and eligible to work, Tia was hired to work part time at Fresh Acres Market and the Sixteen Acres Library until graduation.

On May 19, Jacki, Tia and Tia's mother watched in their home the royal wedding of Meghan Markel and Prince Harry. The three of them celebrated the historic British traditions combined with the modern aspects of the ceremony, rejoicing with the world in the union of the happy couple.

* * *

Tia and Jacki exchanged texts on the evening of May 22, 2018:

Tia: Today is first anniversary of the Manchester, England, terrorist bombing at Ariana Grande's concert.

Jacki: I remember. A terrible day!

Tia: I was amazed that she put on a concert soon after to benefit the families that were affected- 22 killed and more than 500 injured.

Jacki: She named the concert One Love Manchester. 50,000 people attended. Streamed around the world. She did not let terrorist stop people being together.

Tia: Two of my favorite albums of hers- "Yours Truly" and" My Everything."

Jacki: Same here. Also "Dangerous Woman".

Tia: I loved her next album "Sweetener"! She became more creative and free to write new songs. So resilient and remarkable!

Jacki: Ariana said "When you're handed a challenge, instead of sitting there and complaining about it, why not try to make something beautiful."

At the end of May, Tia attended the JROTC Annual Awards/Graduation Night. Many of the cadets received awards of ribbons, medals and certificates and a photo with a national representative presenting the award. Each senior cadet was then introduced and walked under the Sabers for the last time and was then given a Silver and Blue graduation cord. The entire senior year had been very significant for Tia.

Summer 2018

June 20th was the official end of the school year. Tia's graduation celebration was at Springfield Symphony Hall. There were 411 young people in her graduating class. 387 were going on to college and 21 were entering the Armed Forces and/or the work force. Her senior class had secured over $5 million in scholarships. Tia proudly declared "I am the first female in my family going on to college. Both of my parents had completed high school. My father had enlisted in the Army where he continued his education. My mother studied accounting with two years in college and had a career as an accountant. My brother Javier was a couple of years ahead of me in college in Boston."

One of the biggest news stories of the Central class of 2018: Nyasia Jordan was the first generation of her family to attend college, had a 4.4 GPA, received $300,000 in scholarships to Harvard University, had grown up in poverty, and at graduation was recognized as the first African American Valedictorian in the history of Springfield Central High School.

Tia planned to spend the summer working full time at the Sixteen Acres Library and Fresh Acres Market. She planned a one-week road trip with her parents during their vacation from MGM. Although Tia and Jacki were still close friends, they knew that they would be on different paths in the year ahead. They did spend some time together in the summer. Jacki had enlisted in the Air Force and would be attending U Mass Amherst. Most of their mutual friends were scattering to several different schools, most in New England. But they were also aware their future studies and work lives would probably take them on different paths. Each one knew her senior year at Central was one of the best years of her life.

The next morning after graduation Tia was sad because school was all over and she was aware that she may not see many of her classmates in the summer. She was glad that her twelve years of public school studies were completed. She was happy to be starting a brand new chapter as a freshman at Springfield College where she would certainly make new friends and learn much more.

ABOUT THE AUTHOR

ROBERT LOESCH is a United Church of Christ clergyman who has lived and worked in Massachusetts, Connecticut and upstate New York. Most of his career has been in parish ministry and human services. He has traveled extensively in the United States and in more that forty countries. Most of his published writing has been non-fiction. His first collection of short stories *The Day the Drum Stopped and Other Stories* was published in 2013 by The Troy Book Makers. *Out On A Limb and Other Stories* is his second collection of short stories.

To order a copy of either of these books or for other information, please contact:

Robert Loesch
385 Worthington St, Unit 3E
Springfield, MA 01103
rkloesch@aol.com | (518)674-8204